A2 Chemistry
UNIT 4

Edexcel Nuffield

Unit 4: Energy and Reactions

Frank Harriss and Philip Jackson

Philip Allan Updates
Market Place
Deddington
Oxfordshire
OX15 0SE

tel: 01869 338652
fax: 01869 337590
e-mail: sales@philipallan.co.uk
www.philipallan.co.uk

ISBN-13: 978-1-84489-015-6
ISBN-10: 1-84489-015-5

This guide has been written specifically to support students preparing for the Edexcel Nuffield A2 Chemistry Unit 4 examination. The content has been neither approved nor endorsed by Edexcel and remains the sole responsibility of the authors.

Printed by Raithby Lawrence & Co. Ltd, Leicester

Environmental information
The paper on which this title is printed is sourced from managed, sustainable forests.

P00492

Contents

Introduction

■ ■ ■

Content Guidance

■ ■ ■

Questions and Answers

Introduction

About this guide

This guide is designed to help you prepare for the first Nuffield A2 Chemistry unit test, which examines the content of **Unit 4: Energy and Reactions**.

The aim of this guide is to provide you with a clear understanding of the requirements of the unit and to advise you on how best to meet those requirements.

The book is divided into the following sections:
- This **Introduction**, which outlines revision and examination technique, showing you how to prepare for the unit test.
- **Content Guidance**, which provides a summary of all the 'chemical ideas' covered in Unit 4.
- **Questions and Answers**, in which you will find questions in the same style as in the unit test, followed by the answers of two students, one of whom is likely to get an A grade, the other a C/D grade. Examiner's comments follow each of these answers.

How to use this guide

- Begin by reading the section 'Revision and examination technique' in this Introduction.
- Decide on the amount of time you have available for chemistry revision.
- Allocate suitable amounts of time to:
  - each section of the Content Guidance, giving the most time to the areas that seem most unfamiliar
  - the questions in the Questions and Answers section
- Draw up a revision timetable, allocating the time for questions later in your timetable.
- When revising sections of the Content Guidance:
  - read the guidance and look at corresponding sections in your notes and textbooks
  - write your own revision notes
  - try questions from past unit tests and from other sources, such as the *Students' Book*
- When using the Questions and Answers:
  - try to answer the question yourself
  - then look at the students' answers, together with your own, and try to work out the best answer
  - then look at the examiner's comments

Revision and examination technique

How do I find what to learn?

Well, we hope this book will be useful to you! Other sources are:

- the specification. This is the definitive one. If it's not in the skills section of the specification, it won't be in the paper! However, the specification is written in 'examiner-speak', so it might not always be absolutely clear what is required. This guide should help you to interpret the unit content — every specification point is covered in the Content Guidance section.
- the summaries of Key Principles at the end of the topics in the *Students' Book*.
- your own and your teacher's notes. Preparation for an exam is not just something you do shortly before you take the paper. It should be an integral part of your daily work in chemistry.
- revision material can also be found at the Nuffield Foundation website:
  www.chemistry-react.org

How much of the *Students' Book* do I need to learn?

You will need most of this, except:

- the fine detail of experimental procedure
- background reading

General revision tips

Revision is a personal thing

What works for one person does not necessarily work for another. You should by now have some idea about which methods suit you, but here are a few ways to set out your revision notes:

- mind maps — ideas radiate out from a central point and are linked together; some people like to colour these in
- notes with bullet points and headings
- small cards with a limited 'bite-size' amount of material on each

Make a plan

Divide your material into sections (the Content Guidance section will help you). Then:

- work out how much time you have available before the exam
- allocate as much time as you can to each section, bearing in mind which sections you feel you nearly understand and which are the most difficult
- fit this in with any revision your teacher is going to do — ask him or her for a summary

Write, write, write!

Whatever you do, make sure that your revision is *active*, not just flipping over the pages saying 'yeah, yeah, I know this already'. Write more revision notes, test yourself (or each other), *try questions*.

Test yourself
- The review questions in the *Students' Book* are useful 'drill exercises' on topics, but are not all like exam questions.
- Past papers are available and they give you a good indication of what you will be facing.
- The Questions and Answers section of this book is designed for this purpose.

Know the enemy — the exam paper

Hopefully, since you will have prepared properly, you will be able to look on the exam as an opportunity to show what you can do, rather than as a battle! Be aware, however, that you must prepare yourself for an exam just as you would for an important sporting contest — be focused. Work hard right through the 90 minutes and do not dwell on difficulties — put them behind you. Try to emerge feeling worn out but happy that you have done your best, even if you have found it difficult (others will probably feel the same way). Then forget it and don't have a postmortem.

There are usually five structured questions. Each question has a 'theme' and includes both short-answer and longer-answer parts.

Nuffield is all about learning chemistry through experiment, so it is right that the exam questions should reflect this. However, some will be based on chemistry in everyday life and others will be more theoretical.

Sometimes the context will come from the *Students' Book*; sometimes it will be a new one. Look carefully at the 'stem' (the introduction at the top of the question). Most of the important facts here will be needed somewhere in the question. Sometimes, small, additional stems are added later. These are important too.

Dealing with different types of question

Short-answer questions
These are the most straightforward, but remember:
- look at the marks available — make one good point per mark.
- look at the number of lines — this gives *some* idea of the length of answer required. Of course, handwriting varies greatly in size, but if you have written two words and there are three lines, you can assume you have not written enough to score full marks!
- don't 'hedge your bets' — if you give two alternative answers, you will not get the marks unless *both* are right. For example, if the answer is 'hydrogen bond' and you write 'hydrogen bond or permanent dipole attractions', you will score zero.
- read the question — don't answer a question that you have made up! Examiners do have kind hearts really, and they are genuinely sorry when they have to award zero for an answer containing good chemistry that is not relevant to the question asked. This is a problem with units that are examined twice a year. There are a lot of past papers around, all asking slightly different questions on the same subject matter. It's all too easy to give the answer to last year's question.

- think before you write — perhaps jot down a few points in the margin. Try to make your points logically.
- punch those points — if you have read any mark schemes you will see that they give examiners advice on the weakest answer that will still just score the mark. Make sure your points are made well and win the mark without requiring a second's hesitation by the examiner.
- try to write clear sentences (though bullet points might be appropriate on some occasions).
- be sure you do not re-state the question — don't use words or phrases directly from the question as part of your explanation.

Command words in questions

A lot of care is taken in choosing which of these words to use, so note them carefully:
- 'state', 'write down', 'give' and 'name' require short answers only
- 'describe' requires an accurate account of the main points, but no explanation
- 'explain' or 'justify' requires chemical reasons for the statement given
- 'suggest' means that you are not expected to know the answer but you should be able to work it out from what you do know
- 'giving reason(s)' requires you to explain why you chose to answer as you did (if 'reasons' in the plural is stated, judge the number required from the number of marks)

Avoid vague answers

Sometimes it is clear that the candidate knows quite a lot about the topic but his or her answer is not focused. Avoid these words:
- 'it' (e.g. 'it is bigger') — give the name of the thing you are describing, otherwise it may not be clear which object in the question is being referred to
- 'harmful' — if you mean 'toxic' or 'poisonous', say so!
- 'environmentally friendly' — say *why* it benefits the environment
- 'expensive' — always justify this word with a reason

Be careful with chemical particles — always think twice whenever you write 'particle', 'atom', 'molecule' or 'ion', and check that you are using the correct term.

If in doubt, write something

Try to avoid leaving any gaps. Have a go at every answer. If you are not sure, write something that seems to be sensible chemistry. As you will see from the Questions and Answers section, some questions have a variety of possible answers — the only answer that definitely scores zero is a blank.

Diagrams

You would be amazed at some of the diagrams examiners have to mark, so please:
- read the question. The answer is not always a reflux condenser! If it is a piece of apparatus you know, then it is relatively straightforward. If you have to design something, look for clues in the question.
- make it clear and neat. Use a pencil and a ruler, and have a soft rubber handy to erase any errors.

- make sure it looks like real apparatus (which never has square corners, for example). Some apparatus drawn in exams would test the skill of the most proficient glass-blower.
- draw a cross-section, so that gases can have a clear path through. Don't carelessly leave any gaps where gases could leak out.
- think of safety. Don't suggest heating an enclosed apparatus, which would explode. If a poisonous gas is given off, show it being released in a fume cupboard.
- always label your diagram, especially if the question tells you to. Important things to label are substances and calibrated vessels (e.g. syringes or measuring cylinders).

Calculations

It is easy to make mistakes, especially under the pressure of exams. So, set out the steps in your calculations clearly. Then you will get most of the marks if you make a slight mistake and the examiner can see what you are doing. Examiners operate a system called 'transferred error' whereby, once an error has been made, the rest of the calculation scores marks if the method is correct from then on.

When you write down your numerical answer, check:

- **units** — most physical quantities have them, for example $g\,mol^{-1}$, $kJ\,mol^{-1}$
- **sign** (remember that ΔS and ΔH values must be shown as '+' if they are positive)
- **significant figures** — you may be expected to analyse uncertainties more carefully in your practical work, but in exam papers all you have to do is to give the same number of significant figures as the data in the question

One final tip

Remember that Unit Test 4 is an A2 paper and, therefore, a higher standard of answer is required than at AS.

On-line marking

Most Nuffield papers are now marked by examiners on-line. This means that each examiner sees only a little bit of your script, not the whole paper. To avoid losing marks on this new system:

- write in a dark colour (it shows up more clearly on screen)
- give clear, legible answers which will show up well on screen
- write (or draw) your answers within the box laid out on the paper
- if you make a mistake, cross out your answer clearly
- having made a mistake, you may have to rewrite your answer elsewhere on the paper — make it very obvious that you have done this and state clearly where on the paper your rewritten answer can be found (the examiner sees only the tiny bit of the box where your answer is expected to be)

Content
Guidance

The material in this section summarises the chemical concepts from **Unit 4: Energy and Reactions**. Note that each section of the Nuffield specification brings in chemical ideas from a variety of topic areas. This content guidance section is divided into chemical topics, which in some cases link ideas from more than one section of the specification.

Summary of content

Rates of reaction: the effect of concentration on the rate of reaction; measuring rates of reaction; reaction mechanisms; the effect of temperature on the rate of reaction; collision theory; catalysis

Arenes: bonding in benzene; reactions of arenes; phenol

Entropy: entropy changes in the system; entropy changes in the surroundings; the total entropy change

Chemical equilibrium: dynamic equilibrium; the equilibrium law; heterogeneous equilibria; equilibrium and entropy

Acid–base equilibria: conjugate acid–base pairs; the ionisation constant for water; pH; strong and weak acids and bases; acid–base titration curves; buffer solutions

Oxidation products of alcohols: carbonyl compounds; reactions of aldehydes and ketones; carboxylic acids; carboxylic acid derivatives; infrared spectra

How much of this do I need to learn?

The answer is: virtually all of it. It has been pared down to the absolute essentials. If you need any more detail on any aspect, you should look in your textbooks or notes.

Rates of reaction

There has been a question about reaction rates on every Unit Test 4 paper set so far. The questions have always been straightforward.

At GCSE, you learned that the rate of a chemical reaction depends on:
- **particle size** — the smaller the particles of solid, the larger the surface area, the faster the reaction
- **concentration** — the greater the concentration, the more frequent the collisions between reacting particles, the faster the reaction
- **temperature** — the higher the temperature, the faster the particles move, the more frequent the collisions, the faster the reaction
- presence of a **catalyst** — catalysts increase the rate of reaction without being used up

This topic deals with the same ideas but looks at them in greater detail.

Effect of concentration on rate of reaction

The topic is dominated by graphs. It is important to be able to sketch them, to understand them and to be able to draw them accurately from given data.

If A and B react together to form C and D, the rate can be stated in terms of:
- the rate at which either A or B is used up
- the rate at which C or D is formed

Usually, the rate is stated in terms of the change in concentration (of a substance) per unit time, for example:

$mol\, dm^{-3}\, s^{-1}$

If the concentration of A is doubled, the effect on the rate could be that:
- the rate doubles
- the rate stays constant
- the rate quadruples

On doubling the concentration of A, if the rate doubles it means that the rate is **directly proportional** to the concentration of A. A graph of rate against concentration of A is a straight line, with a positive gradient (slope).

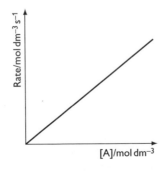

The reaction is said to be **first order** with respect to A:

rate $\propto [A]^1$

If the rate stays constant, it means that changing the concentration of A has no effect on the rate. A graph of rate against concentration of A is a horizontal, straight line.

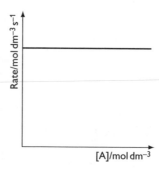

The reaction is said to be **zero order** with respect to A:

rate $\propto [A]^0$

If the rate quadruples, a graph of rate against concentration of A is a curve.

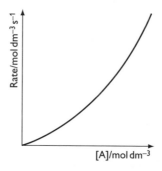

A graph of the rate of reaction against the square of the concentration of A is a straight line with a positive slope. This means that the rate is **directly proportional** to the square of the concentration of A.

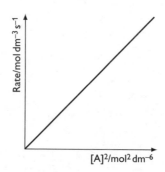

The reaction is said to be **second order** with respect to A:

rate $\propto [A]^2$

Series of experiments can be carried out to determine:

- how the rate of reaction changes when the concentration of A is changed (while the concentration of B is kept constant)
- how the rate of reaction changes when the concentration of B is changed (while the concentration of A is kept constant)

From such experiments, the order of reaction with respect to both A and B can be found.

The **rate equation** for the reaction can then be written. For example:

$$\text{rate} = k[A][B]^2$$

where k is the **rate constant** (the 'proportional' sign is replaced by an 'equals' sign). [A] indicates that the reaction is first order with respect to A (the index, 1, is usually omitted). $[B]^2$ indicates that the reaction is second order with respect to B. Overall, the reaction is third order — the individual orders are added together.

Orders of reaction cannot be predicted by looking at the balanced chemical equation. They can be found only by experiment.

Working out half-lives

Instead of carrying out series of experiments using different concentrations of A and B and finding the resulting rates of reaction, a single experiment can be carried out in which the concentration of A (or B) is measured as the reaction proceeds. There are three possible types of graph to represent such an experiment.

If the reaction is first order with respect to A, then a graph like the one below is obtained.

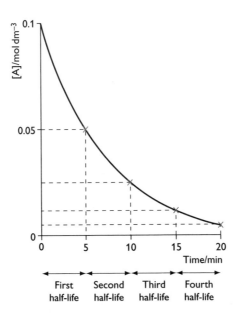

On this graph the time taken for the concentration of A to decrease from $0.1\,\text{mol}\,\text{dm}^{-3}$ to half this value ($0.05\,\text{mol}\,\text{dm}^{-3}$) is 5 minutes. This is called the **half-life**.

The time taken for the concentration of A to decrease from $0.05\,mol\,dm^{-3}$ to half this value $(0.025\,mol\,dm^{-3})$ is also 5 minutes. Again, this is the half-life (but starting from a different concentration). Thus, the half-life is a constant. This means the reaction is first order with respect to the concentration of A.

Tip Avoid the common mistake of drawing a half-life graph such as this and then saying that the second half-life is 10 minutes.

Another possible shape for the graph is:

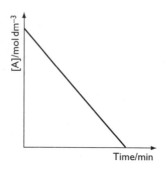

A straight-line graph such as the one above means that the reaction is zero order with respect to the concentration of A. (A is used up at the same rate throughout the reaction. Therefore, its decreasing concentration does not affect the rate.)

A third possible shape for the graph is a sharper curve.

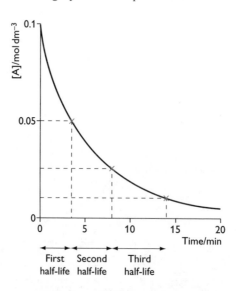

Here, the half-lives for the curve increase significantly — each successive half-life is longer than the previous half-life. This means that the reaction is probably second order with respect to the concentration of A.

Methods for measuring rates of reaction (following a reaction)

A reaction can be followed by measuring a property that shows a significant change during the reaction. For example:

- The volume of gas in a gas syringe can be measured at set time intervals.

Tip This is a common method, so make sure you can draw the apparatus correctly.

- If the reaction produces or uses up ions as it proceeds, the electrical conductivity at set time intervals could be measured.
- There may be a colour change as the reaction proceeds. This could be measured at set time intervals using a colorimeter.
- Production or loss of a substance (e.g. H^+ or OH^-) can be measured by:
  - taking samples at given time intervals
  - quenching them with a large volume of ice-cold water (to stop the reaction, so that the measurement applies to the chosen time)
  - titrating with a known concentration of an appropriate reagent (e.g. $0.1 \, mol \, dm^{-3}$ NaOH if the rate of production of H^+ is being measured)

A graph is then drawn of the property that changes (vertical axis) against time (horizontal axis). A tangent drawn against this curve at any point is the rate at that time. The tangent is usually drawn through the origin and the gradient is then the initial rate.

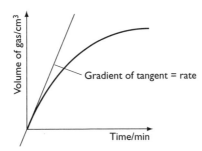

Reaction mechanisms

Rate-determining step

Some reactions happen in two or more steps or stages. When put together, these steps form the **mechanism** of the reaction. For example:

Step 1: reactants A + B $\longrightarrow$ intermediate AB
Step 2: intermediate AB $\longrightarrow$ products C + D

One of these steps will be slower than the other and will act as a bottleneck. The other step(s) in a reaction can only go as fast as the slow step produces the intermediate. Therefore, the slow step controls the overall rate of the reaction and is called the **rate-determining step**.

The concentrations of the substances involved in the rate-determining step control the rate of this slow step and thus control the overall rate of reaction.

Hydrolysis of a primary halogenoalkane by hydroxide ions: S_N2 mechanism

The hydrolysis of 1-bromobutane by hydroxide ions is represented by the equation:

$$C_4H_9Br + OH^- \longrightarrow C_4H_9OH + Br^-$$

In a series of experiments, the following initial rates were obtained.

Experiment	Concentration of 1-bromobutane/ mol dm^{-3}	Concentration of hydroxide ions/ mol dm^{-3}	Initial rate of reaction/ mol dm^{-3} s^{-1}
1	0.1	0.1	0.001
2	0.2	0.1	0.002
3	0.2	0.2	0.004

- Comparing experiments 1 and 2 — doubling the concentration of 1-bromobutane (while keeping the concentration of hydroxide constant) doubles the rate. Therefore, the reaction is first order with respect to 1-bromobutane.
- Comparing experiments 2 and 3 — doubling the concentration of hydroxide ions (while keeping the concentration of 1-bromobutane constant) also doubles the rate. Therefore, the reaction is first order with respect to hydroxide ions.

So, the rate equation is:

rate = k[1-bromobutane][OH$^-$]

Overall, the reaction is second order. This means that the rate-determining step must involve both 1-bromobutane and hydroxide ions. A mechanism that fits this result is:

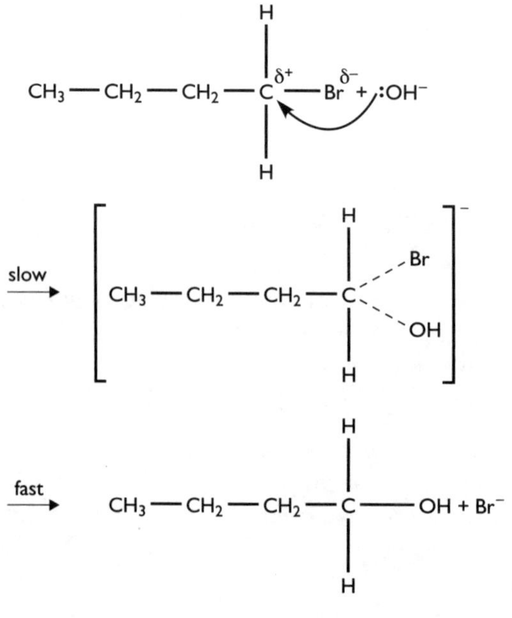

- The reaction is a substitution.
- It is nucleophilic.
- The rate-determining step involves two species.

Therefore, the mechanism is called an S_N2 mechanism.

Hydrolysis of a tertiary halogenoalkane by hydroxide ions: S_N1 mechanism

Suppose the hydrolysis experiments were repeated using 2-bromo-2-methylpropane instead of 1-bromobutane. The results are shown in the table below.

Experiment	Concentration of 2-bromo-2-methylpropane/ mol dm^{-3}	Concentration of hydroxide ions/ mol dm^{-3}	Initial rate of reaction/ mol dm^{-3} s^{-1}
1	0.1	0.1	0.001
2	0.2	0.1	0.002
3	0.2	0.2	0.002

- Comparing experiments 1 and 2 — doubling the concentration of 2-bromo-2-methyl-propane (while keeping the concentration of hydroxide constant) doubles the rate. Therefore, the reaction is first order with respect to 2-bromo-2-methylpropane.
- Comparing experiments 2 and 3 — doubling the concentration of hydroxide ions (while keeping the concentration of 2-bromo-2-methylpropane constant) does *not* affect the rate. This means that the reaction is zero order with respect to hydroxide ions.

So, the rate equation is:

rate = k[2-bromo-2-methylpropane]

The rate-determining step involves only 2-bromo-2-methylpropane and not hydroxide. A mechanism that is consistent with this result is:

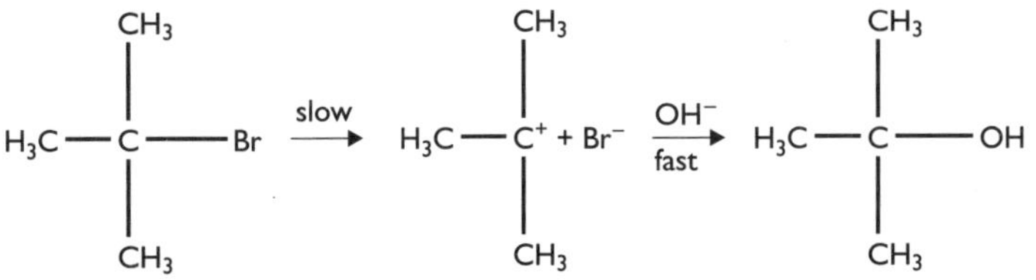

This is a nucleophilic substitution with only one species involved in the rate-determining step. Therefore, it is an S_N1 mechanism.

Effect of temperature on rate of reaction

The rate of a chemical reaction increases when the temperature is increased, because:

- An increase in temperature increases the kinetic energy of the particles, which therefore move faster. If the particles move faster, they collide more often. Particles react only when they collide. Therefore, if they collide more often the reaction will be faster.

Tip When you are writing about this, do *not* say that the particles 'collide more'. Time is important. You must say that the particles collide more *often* or more *frequently*.

- For a reaction to occur between two particles, collision alone is not enough. Particles must collide with sufficient energy for bonds to be broken. The minimum kinetic energy that colliding particles must possess for the process of bond breaking (and thus the reaction) to begin is called the **activation energy, E_A**. The activation energy can be thought of as the stimulus that the reaction needs to get going. A simple example of such a stimulus is striking a match to get it to burn (the friction generates heat).

Activation energy is shown on the graph below.

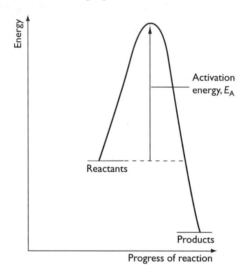

The activation energy for a given reaction mechanism is fixed.

The effect of raising the temperature on the energy of the particles is shown by the Maxwell–Boltzmann distribution of molecular energies in the following graph.

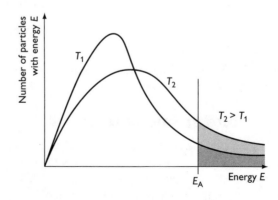

Tip In the unit test, you may be asked to reproduce a sketch of this graph. For full marks, the sketch has to be accurate, i.e. it must start at the origin and, as the value of E increases, the curve must never touch the horizontal axis.

The activation energy is shown on the energy (horizontal) axis. At temperature T_1, the number of particles with energy greater than the activation energy is relatively small. At a higher temperature (T_2), the peak is lower and further to the right, and a greater number of particles have a kinetic energy greater than the activation energy. Therefore, the frequency (time again!) of *effective* collisions increases.

Being able to draw this graph accurately and explain its significance could be worth a lot of marks.

Determining the activation energy for a reaction
This relies on the **Arrhenius equation**.

Tip You do not need to learn this equation. If it is needed in the unit test, it will be given. However, you are expected to be able to use it.

The Arrhenius equation has two interchangeable forms that you need to be able to recognise. One form is:

rate = $Ae^{-E_A/RT}$

where A is a constant which we tend to ignore, e is the exponential function, R is the gas constant and T is the temperature.

This looks horrendous, so to make it easier to use we take natural logarithms:

ln rate = ln A – E_A/RT

This still looks horrendous until you realise that it is a straight-line graph equation of the form:

$y = mx + c$

where y is ln rate, c is ln A, x is $1/T$ and m (the gradient) is $-E_A/R$.

Plotting a graph of ln rate against $1/T$ in kelvin produces a straight line with a negative gradient, as shown below.

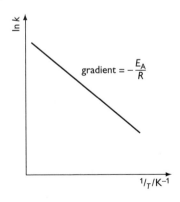

In the unit test, you may be given the results of such an experiment and asked to find the activation energy. There are a number of things to be careful of here:

- Use all the results that are given.
- Label the axes fully, including units (which are K^{-1} for $1/T$).
- Remember that the values of $1/T$ will be very small (of the order of 0.003).
- Calculate the gradient using the largest values you can (to minimise errors).

$$\text{gradient} = \frac{\text{change on vertical axis}}{\text{change on horizontal axis}}$$

In these calculations, the gradient will be a large negative number (because it is a negative gradient and $1/T$ is very small).

Example

Suppose the gradient = $-10\,000$.

Then, $-10\,000 = -E_A/R$
  $R = 8.314\,J\,mol^{-1}\,K^{-1}$
  $E_A = 8.314 \times 10\,000$ (the two minus signs cancel out)
  $E_A = 83\,140\,J\,mol^{-1} = +83.1\,kJ\,mol^{-1}$
(R, the gas constant, will be provided in the question.)

Tip Remember:

- Watch out for the number of significant figures demanded by the question. After all this hard work it would be silly to lose a mark by using the wrong number of significant figures in your answer.
- Activation energies are always positive, so put the '+' sign in.
- Always include the units — not doing so is another silly way to lose marks.

Catalysis

There are two types of catalysis.

Homogeneous catalysis

In **homogeneous catalysis**, the catalyst and the reactants are in the same phase. An example is the synthesis of an ester from a carboxylic acid and an alcohol, using hydrogen ions as the catalyst. The reactants and catalyst are all in aqueous solution.

Heterogeneous catalysis

In **heterogeneous catalysis**, the catalyst is in a different phase from the reactants. An example is the use of a solid iron catalyst in the reaction between gaseous hydrogen and nitrogen to form ammonia by the Haber process.

How do catalysts work?

Catalysts work by providing an **alternative mechanism** that has a lower activation energy than that of the uncatalysed reaction.

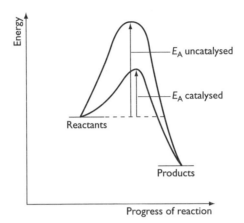

The catalytic mechanism has a lower activation energy, so more particles have energy greater than this new activation energy. Therefore, the frequency of effective collisions is greater and the rate of reaction is faster.

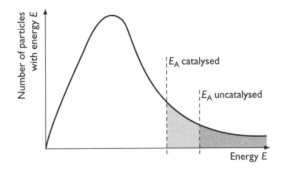

Note: Catalysts do *not* work by lowering the activation energy of a reaction. *Do not* write this!

Arenes: benzene and phenol

Bonding in benzene

The molecular formula of benzene is C_6H_6. Each molecule consists of a ring of six carbon atoms each of which is bonded to one hydrogen atom.

Kekulé described the bonding between the carbon atoms as being alternate single and double bonds.

Evidence against the Kekulé structure

There are several lines of evidence that suggest that this structure is incorrect.

Structural evidence

If the Kekulé structure were correct, **X-ray diffraction** studies would be expected to reveal two different carbon-to-carbon bond lengths:

- C–C   0.15 nm
- C=C   0.13 nm

In fact, only one bond length is found. The carbon-to-carbon bond length in benzene is 0.14 nm.

Similarly, the **infrared spectrum** of benzene does not show an absorption corresponding to the C=C bond. However, it does show absorption from a carbon-to-carbon bond that is not present in either alkanes or alkenes.

Thermodynamic studies

When the C=C double bond in cyclohexene is hydrogenated, the enthalpy change for the reaction ($\Delta H^{\ominus}_{\text{reaction}}$) is –120 kJ mol^{-1}.

$$\bigcirc + H_2 \longrightarrow \bigcirc \qquad \Delta H^{\ominus}_{\text{reaction}} = -120\,\text{kJ mol}^{-1}$$

If the Kekulé formula were correct, the enthalpy change ($\Delta H^{\ominus}_{\text{reaction}}$) for the hydrogenation of benzene would be expected to be three times this value, i.e. –360 kJ mol^{-1}.

$$\bigcirc + 3H_2 \longrightarrow \bigcirc \qquad \Delta H^{\ominus}_{\text{reaction}} = -360\,\text{kJ mol}^{-1}$$

Cyclohexa-1,3,5-triene

However, the experimental value for the enthalpy change for the hydrogenation of benzene is found to be –208 kJ mol^{-1}. This means that benzene is much more stable than expected from the Kekulé formula.

Chemical evidence

Unlike alkenes, benzene does not undergo electrophilic addition reactions typical of C=C compounds. Instead it undergoes electrophilic substitution reactions.

Delocalisation in benzene

The evidence suggests that benzene has **delocalised electrons**. Each carbon atom in benzene forms three covalent sigma bonds (one to a hydrogen atom and one to each of its two neighbouring carbon atoms). Therefore, three of the four bonding electrons of each carbon atom have been used. The unused electron is a *p*-orbital electron. Overall, in a benzene ring there are six of these (one from each carbon atom). These six electrons form a delocalised electron cloud above and below the ring.

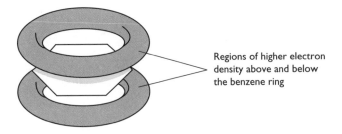

Regions of higher electron density above and below the benzene ring

The presence of this cloud of negative charge above and below the ring has a great effect on how benzene reacts. It is this delocalisation that makes benzene more stable than expected. The presence of the six delocalised electrons means that benzene is susceptible to attack by species that need electrons (electrophiles).

Reactions of arenes

Benzene is carcinogenic and its use in school laboratories is prohibited. Methyl-benzene or methoxybenzene, which are chemically similar to benzene, are used in experiments.

Combustion

Benzene is highly flammable and burns with a sooty flame because it has a high carbon:hydrogen ratio. As with other hydrocarbons, complete combustion gives carbon dioxide and water; incomplete combustion gives carbon monoxide (or carbon) and water.

$$C_6H_6(l) + 7\frac{1}{2}O_2(g) \longrightarrow 6CO_2(g) + 3H_2O(l)$$

Substitution reactions

Action of bromine

Since benzene is stable compared with alkenes, the reaction between benzene and bromine requires a catalyst and the bromine is *liquid* bromine (not bromine solution). The catalyst is iron.

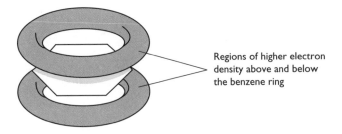

Bromobenzene

This is a substitution reaction in which one of the hydrogen atoms in the benzene ring is replaced by a bromine atom. The products are 1-bromobenzene and hydrogen bromide (which produces white fumes with ammonia gas).

Action of concentrated nitric acid and concentrated sulphuric acid (nitrating mixture)

In this substitution reaction (known as **nitration**) the sulphuric acid acts as a catalyst.

Nitrobenzene

A single hydrogen atom is replaced by a nitro group. If the reaction is performed at higher temperatures, further substitution of hydrogen atoms by nitro groups occurs. The products of such reactions can be used as explosives — for example, TNT.

Action of concentrated sulphuric acid

This **sulphonation** reaction requires extreme conditions. Benzene is heated under reflux with a solution of sulphur trioxide in concentrated sulphuric acid ('fuming' sulphuric acid) for several hours.

Benzenesulphonic acid

The product is benzenesulphonic acid. Starting with methoxybenzene, the product would be methoxybenzenesulphonic acid. Such compounds are used to make detergents, drugs and dyes.

Action of a halogenoalkane

The reaction between benzene and a halogenoalkane is an **alkylation** reaction. Aluminium chloride is used as the catalyst.

Methylbenzene

This is also a substitution reaction — a hydrogen atom is replaced by an alkyl group (in this case a methyl group).

Reactions of this type are called **Friedel–Crafts reactions**.

The mechanism of electrophilic substitution

The substitution reactions described above are all **electrophilic substitution** reactions. You should be prepared to explain these two words.

- **Substitution** occurs when one atom (or group of atoms) is replaced by another atom (or group of atoms).

Tip Do not use the word 'substitute' to explain substitution. In a recent unit test many students did this and did not score the mark.

- An **electrophile** is an electron-deficient species. It may have a positive charge or a $\delta+$ charge.

There are two stages in an electrophilic substitution mechanism:
- creation of the electrophile
- attack by the electrophile on the benzene ring

For example, in bromination the first stage of the reaction is the oxidation of the iron catalyst by bromine:

$$2Fe + 3Br_2 \longrightarrow 2FeBr_3$$

$FeBr_3$ can then polarise another bromine molecule:

$$FeBr_3 + Br_2 \longrightarrow Br^{\delta+}\!-\!Br^{\delta-}.FeBr_3$$

It is the $Br^{\delta+}$ which is the electrophile and this goes on to attack the benzene ring.

The catalyst is really $FeBr_3$ and its function is to provide an electron-deficient bromine atom.

In a Friedel–Crafts alkylation, the function of the aluminium chloride catalyst is to produce an electron-deficient alkyl group:

$$CH_3CH_2Cl + AlCl_3 \longrightarrow CH_3CH_2^+AlCl_4^-$$

The electrophile is $CH_3CH_2^+$, which then attacks the electron-rich benzene ring.

Summary

The electrophilic substitution reactions of arenes, as exemplified by benzene, are summarised in the table below.

Reagent	Catalyst	Electrophile	Product
Liquid bromine	Fe or $FeBr_3$	$Br^{\delta+}$	Bromobenzene
Concentrated nitric acid	Concentrated sulphuric acid	Nitronium ion, NO_2^+	Nitrobenzene
Fuming sulphuric acid	—	Sulphur trioxide, SO_3	Benzenesulphonic acid
Chloroethane	$AlCl_3$	$CH_3CH_2^+$	Ethylbenzene

Addition reactions of the benzene ring

Action of hydrogen

The product is cyclohexane, which is used to make nylon.

Action of chlorine

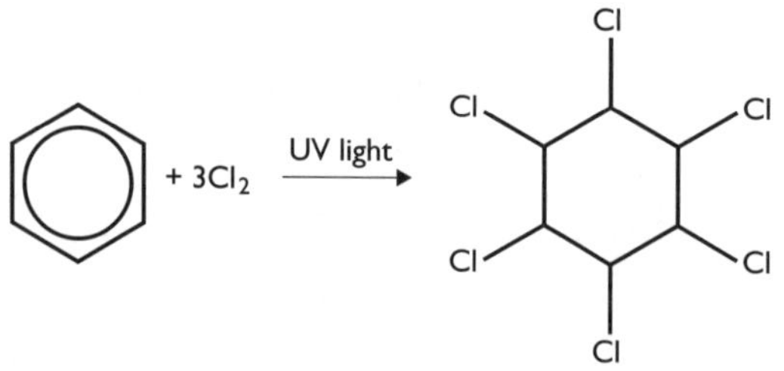

This is a free radical reaction. The product is 1,2,3,4,5,6-hexachlorocyclohexane, which is used as an insecticide.

Phenol

A molecule of phenol is a benzene ring with an –OH group in place of one of the hydrogen atoms. However, phenol is *not* an alcohol.

One of the lone pairs of electrons on the oxygen becomes part of the delocalised system, joining the six delocalised electrons from the benzene ring. This affects the properties of both the benzene ring and the –OH group.

Solubility

Phenol is a solid at room temperature. It can form hydrogen bonds with water, but the benzene ring limits its solubility. A solution of phenol in hot water is very slightly acidic.

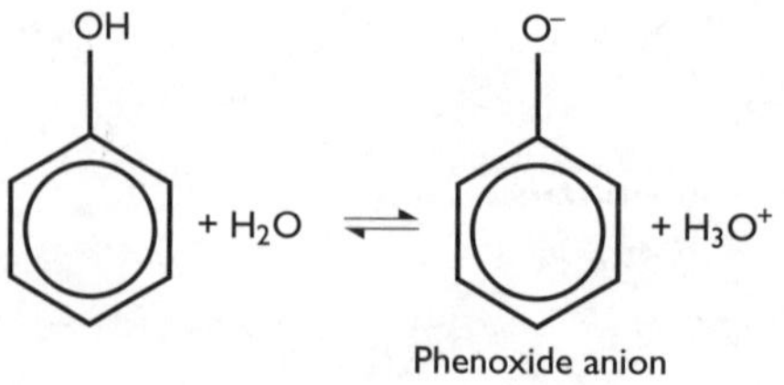

Phenoxide anion

The formation of the phenoxide anion is possible because its negative charge can become delocalised around the benzene ring and this very slightly increases the stability of the anion.

Phenol as an acid

Phenol is a very weak acid.

Action of sodium

Sodium reacts with *molten* phenol. There is effervescence and the sodium disappears.

The products are sodium phenoxide (an *ionic* salt) and hydrogen.

Tip Be very careful when you draw the formula of sodium phenoxide. Show the charges on the oxygen and the sodium ion and do *not* put a covalent bond between them.

Action of aqueous sodium hydroxide

Phenol dissolves readily in a solution of sodium hydroxide, reacting with it to produce sodium phenoxide and water.

Action of sodium carbonate solution

Acids such as ethanoic acid react with carbonates to evolve carbon dioxide gas. However, with phenol there is no reaction. This is because phenol is such a weak acid that it cannot react with carbonates.

Ester formation

Alcohols such as ethanol react with carboxylic acids (e.g. ethanoic acid) to form esters. This is a nucleophilic reaction in which a lone pair of electrons on the oxygen atom of the alcohol –OH group attacks the $C^{\delta+}$ of the carboxyl group.

In phenol, the lone pair on the oxygen atom is involved in the delocalised electron system of the benzene ring and is, therefore, less available to attack the $C^{\delta+}$ of the carboxyl group. This means that phenol is not a good nucleophile.

However, the phenoxide anion, with its negative charge, is a much better nucleophile than phenol. Therefore, to synthesise a phenyl ester (e.g. phenyl ethanoate), the phenol is dissolved in sodium hydroxide solution first. Ethanoic anhydride is used, rather than ethanoic acid, because it is more reactive.

Ethanoic anhydride

Phenyl ethanoate

Comparing phenol with ethanol

- Ethanol reacts with HBr according to the equation:

$$C_2H_5OH + HBr \longrightarrow C_2H_5Br + H_2O$$

Phenol does not react with HBr. This is because the delocalisation of the lone pair of electrons on the oxygen atom into the electron system of the benzene ring increases the strength of the C–O bond. This makes it more difficult to break than the equivalent bond in ethanol, where no such delocalisation is possible.

- Ethanol undergoes oxidation easily, forming ethanal or ethanoic acid. Phenol does not undergo oxidation, because it would require disruption of the very stable benzene ring.

- Ethanol undergoes an elimination reaction (dehydration) to form ethene. Again, phenol does not do this because it would require disruption of the benzene ring.

Property	Ethanol, C_2H_5OH	Phenol, C_6H_5OH
Solubility in water	Soluble in all proportions	Only sparingly soluble
pH of aqueous solution	Neutral	Slightly acidic, 6.5
Action of sodium	Sodium ethoxide and hydrogen	Sodium phenoxide and hydrogen
Action of sodium hydroxide solution	No reaction	Sodium phenoxide and water
Ester formation	Good nucleophile Reacts with carboxylic acid with H⁺ catalyst	Poor nucleophile Dissolves in sodium hydroxide solution and then reacts with ethanoic anhydride
Reaction with hydrogen halide (e.g. HBr)	Forms halogenoalkanes readily	Does not react
Oxidation with potassium dichromate and sulphuric acid	Easily oxidised to ethanal and ethanoic acid	No oxidation
Dehydration by Al_2O_3 at 400°C	Easily dehydrated to ethene	No dehydration possible

Reactions of the benzene ring in phenol

The benzene ring in phenol has its own six delocalised electrons and a share in the two delocalised electrons from the oxygen atom. Therefore, there is more negative charge above and below the ring in phenol than there is in benzene itself. Phenol is, therefore, more susceptible to attack by electrophiles. This means that the extreme conditions needed to make benzene react are not needed with phenol.

Reagent	Conditions for bromination	Conditions for nitration
Benzene	Liquid bromine with iron catalyst	Concentrated nitric acid with concentrated sulphuric acid catalyst
Phenol	Aqueous bromine	Dilute nitric acid

In fact, with phenol the reactions occur so readily that multiple substitution often takes place. For example, in bromination:

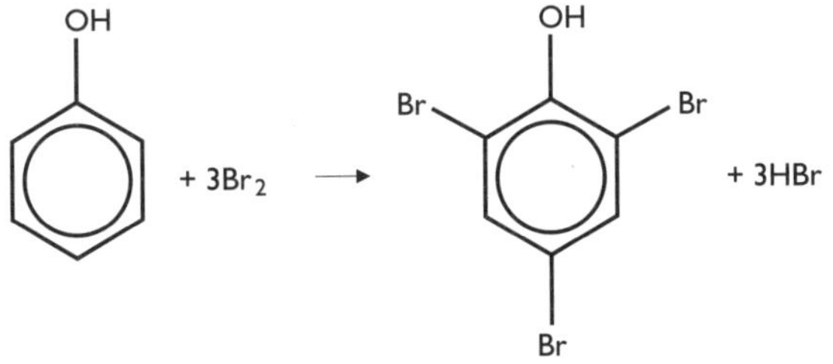

2,4,6-tribromophenol

With nitric acid, two isomers are formed:

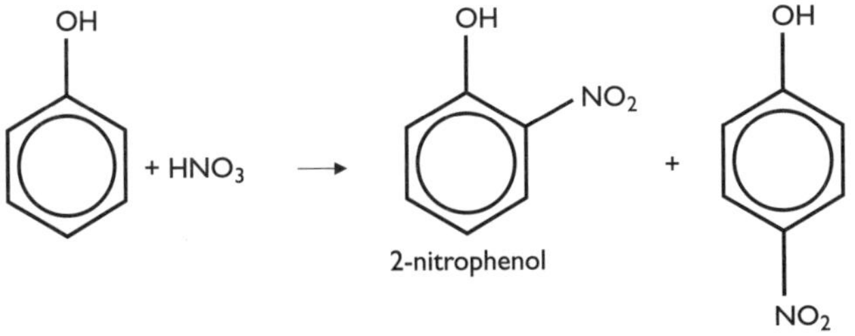

2-nitrophenol

4-nitrophenol

Entropy

The bad news is that entropy is a difficult concept to understand. The good news is that the questions asked about it in the unit test are usually very straightforward.

Entropy is about the number of ways of arranging things, specifically:
- particles in a substance
- quanta of energy

One way to think about entropy is to consider the degree of order of the system:

- A solid is a highly ordered system. There are a limited number of ways in which the particles can be arranged. The particles are fixed in place. A solid thus has a 'low entropy' or low **standard molar entropy** (given the symbol $S^\ominus$).
- A liquid, such as an aqueous solution, is a more disordered system. The particles are free to move around and the number of ways in which they can be arranged is far greater. A liquid therefore has a higher entropy and greater value of $S^\ominus$.
- A gas is the most disordered system possible. The particles have complete freedom to move around and do so very quickly. There are many ways of arranging the particles, so a gas has a very high entropy and value of $S^\ominus$.

Chemical systems tend to change from a highly ordered state (low entropy) to a highly disordered state (high entropy) simply because that is the most probable change by chance alone. There will be an increase in entropy. If a reaction involves an increase in the degree of disorder of particles or an increase in the sharing of quanta of energy, then it is likely to be spontaneous (just happen). Spontaneous reactions have a positive overall entropy change.

Entropy change of the system

Consider the reaction between magnesium metal (a solid and therefore a highly ordered system) and dilute hydrochloric acid (an aqueous solution and therefore a disordered system):

$$Mg(s) + 2HCl(aq) \longrightarrow MgCl_2(aq) + H_2(g)$$

The products are magnesium chloride (in aqueous solution and therefore disordered) and hydrogen gas (a very disordered system).

The standard molar entropy of the two aqueous solutions will be roughly the same. The loss of entropy (because the HCl is used up) is made up for by the gain in entropy from the magnesium chloride. The low standard molar entropy of the magnesium is lost and the very high standard molar entropy of gaseous hydrogen is gained.

Therefore, we can predict that the disorder of the system will increase and that the **entropy change of the system** will be positive, i.e. $\Delta S^\ominus_{system}$ is positive.

Questions that give a reaction and ask you to predict the sign of $\Delta S^\ominus_{system}$ are very common. Always look for a gas because:

- if a gas is produced, $\Delta S^\ominus_{system}$ will probably be positive
- if a gas is used up, $\Delta S^\ominus_{system}$ will probably be negative

Consider the burning of magnesium in air:

$$2Mg(s) + O_2(g) \longrightarrow 2MgO(s)$$

Oxygen is used up, so the prediction is that the system is going from disorder (gas + solid) to greater order (solid). Therefore, $\Delta S^\ominus_{system}$ will be negative.

The question could then ask you to do a calculation to test your prediction. The standard molar entropy values needed are always provided.

Substance	Standard molar entropy, $S^\ominus$/J mol^{-1} K^{-1}
Mg(s)	32.7
$\frac{1}{2}O_2$(g)	102.5
MgO(s)	26.9

Notice the much lower standard entropy values of the solids — fewer ways of arranging the particles.

Values for diatomic gases such as oxygen are always quoted *per mole of atoms*. The values have to be doubled for molecules. Failure to do this is a common mistake. In this example, $\Delta S^\ominus_{system}$ is calculated as follows:

$\Delta S^\ominus_{system} = S^\ominus_{products} - S^\ominus_{reactants}$
$\Delta S^\ominus_{system} = (2 \times 26.9) - (2 \times 32.7) - (2 \times 102.5)$
$\Delta S^\ominus_{system} = -216.6\,\text{J mol}^{-1}\,\text{K}^{-1}$

So the prediction was correct. Notice that the high standard molar entropy of the gas is of great significance to the result.

On making predictions such as these, look at the physical states of the substances (especially look for gases) and at the number of moles. They are important too. For example, consider the reaction:

$2NO(g) + O_2(g) \longrightarrow 2NO_2(g)$

Here, 3 moles of gas are converted into 2 moles of gas. There are more ways of arranging the particles in 3 moles of gas than there are in 2 moles of gas. Therefore, the system is becoming less disordered (more ordered) and $\Delta S^\ominus_{system}$ will be negative.

So far, only the entropy change for the substances involved in the reaction has been considered. Everything else (the solvent, the test tube, the laboratory) is the surroundings.

Entropy change of the surroundings

An exothermic reaction ($-\Delta H$) gives out energy to the surroundings. Quanta of energy are, therefore, being shared out among all the particles in the surroundings. This means that there are now more ways of distributing these quanta of energy because there are far more particles to share them among. The entropy of the surroundings has increased. We say that $\Delta S^\ominus_{surroundings}$ is positive.

- $-\Delta H$ indicates $+\Delta S^\ominus_{surroundings}$

An endothermic reaction ($+\Delta H$) takes in energy from the surroundings. These quanta of energy are now shared among all the particles constituting the system. There are far fewer particles in the system than in the surroundings. Therefore, the number of ways of sharing out the quanta of energy has decreased. The entropy of the surroundings has decreased and $\Delta S^{\ominus}_{surroundings}$ is negative.

- $+\Delta H$ indicates $-\Delta S^{\ominus}_{surroundings}$

The relationship between ΔH and $\Delta S^{\ominus}_{surroundings}$ is:

$$\Delta S^{\ominus}_{surroundings} = \frac{-(\Delta H) \times 1000}{T}$$

This formula has to be learned.

The units for ΔH are **kilojoules** mole^{-1}; the units for ΔS are **joules** mole^{-1} K^{-1}. In calculations, the ΔH value must be multiplied by 1000 to change it to joules.

Tip It is important to remember to do this — students often lose marks because they forget.

For magnesium burning in air, $\Delta H = -1203.4$ kJ mol^{-1}. $\Delta S^{\ominus}_{surroundings}$ is calculated as follows:

$$\Delta S^{\ominus}_{surroundings} = \frac{-(-1203.4) \times 1000}{298}$$
$$= +4038 \, \text{J mol}^{-1} \text{K}^{-1}$$

Total entropy change of the reaction

The total entropy change is found by adding together the entropy change of the system and the entropy change of the surroundings:

$$\Delta S^{\ominus}_{total} = \Delta S^{\ominus}_{system} + \Delta S^{\ominus}_{surroundings}$$

For magnesium burning in air, $\Delta S^{\ominus}_{total}$ is calculated as follows:

$$\Delta S^{\ominus}_{total} = -216.6 + 4038$$
$$= +3821 \, \text{J mol}^{-1} \text{K}^{-1}$$

$\Delta S^{\ominus}_{total}$ is thus positive and so this reaction is **spontaneous**. Any reaction with a positive $\Delta S^{\ominus}_{total}$ will go — although it might go very slowly. Entropy change tells us nothing about rate of reaction.

A reaction with a negative $\Delta S^{\ominus}_{system}$ will be spontaneous provided it is exothermic enough for $\Delta S^{\ominus}_{surroundings}$ to be more positive than $\Delta S^{\ominus}_{system}$ is negative. $\Delta S^{\ominus}_{surroundings}$ is usually the major factor governing whether $\Delta S^{\ominus}_{total}$ is positive or not. Generally, for $\Delta S^{\ominus}_{total}$ to be positive, $\Delta S^{\ominus}_{surroundings}$ must be positive. This explains why most reactions are exothermic.

Reactions with a positive $\Delta S^{\ominus}_{total}$ and negative $\Delta S^{\ominus}_{surroundings}$ (i.e. endothermic) are rare.

Tip If you are asked to compare the relative magnitudes of $\Delta S^{\ominus}_{system}$ and $\Delta S^{\ominus}_{surroundings}$, be careful how you do this. Do *not* write: 'for $\Delta S^{\ominus}_{total}$ to be positive, $\Delta S^{\ominus}_{surroundings}$ must be greater than $\Delta S^{\ominus}_{system}$'. Do write: 'for $\Delta S^{\ominus}_{total}$ to be positive, $\Delta S^{\ominus}_{surroundings}$ must be *more positive* than $\Delta S^{\ominus}_{system}$ is *negative*'.

Chemical equilibrium

In chemistry, many reactions go from reactants (A + B) to products (C + D):

A + B ⟶ C + D

However, there are many reactions in which the products (C + D) can react together too to reform the reactants (A + B):

C + D ⟶ A + B

Such reactions are **reversible** and can be represented by:

A + B ⇌ C + D

Dynamic equilibrium

There are many reactions in which the **forward reaction** (A + B) and the **reverse reaction** (C + D) occur at the same time. If the forward reaction and the reverse reaction are occurring simultaneously and at the same rate, then A and B are being reformed as fast as they are being used up. The same is true of C and D. The reactions are still going on, but overall there is no change in the concentration of A, B, C or D. This is called **dynamic equilibrium**.

An equilibrium reaction never goes to completion, however long it is left. An equilibrium mixture is always formed, which contains the reactants and the products at constant concentrations.

An example of dynamic equilibrium is the Haber process for the manufacture of ammonia:

$N_2(g) + 3H_2(g) \rightleftharpoons 2NH_3(g)$

When this reaction is at equilibrium, for every two molecules of ammonia that are formed, two molecules break down. Therefore, the concentration remains the same.

An equilibrium reaction can remain stable only in a **closed system**, i.e. one in which no material can be lost to, or gained from, the surroundings. If such a change occurs, then the equilibrium will also change. Equilibrium can be approached from either direction, so in the example above you could either start with nitrogen and hydrogen or with ammonia. Either way, the result is an equilibrium mixture.

The equilibrium law

Equilibria vary tremendously. Consider an equilibrium that has mainly reactants but not much product. The equilibrium is said to lie over to the left-hand side of the equation. If there were lots of product but not much reactant, the equilibrium would lie over to the right-hand side. The equilibrium position is defined by the **equilibrium constant**, K_c or K_p.

The equilibrium constant is worked out from the **equilibrium expression**. For example, in the Haber process:

$$N_2(g) + 3H_2(g) \rightleftharpoons 2NH_3(g)$$

$$K_c = \frac{[NH_3(g)]^2_{eqm}}{[N_2(g)]_{eqm} \, [H_2(g)]^3_{eqm}}$$

In the equilibrium expression:
- the square brackets mean concentration in mol dm^{-3}
- the concentrations are raised to the power of the number of molecules in the balanced chemical equation
- '*eqm*' shows that the concentrations are those at equilibrium, rather than those at the start of the reaction
- the products always go above the reactants

Tip When you write an equilibrium expression in an answer to a unit test question, be careful to include state symbols.

K_c is always used with concentrations. Sometimes in reactions involving gases, it is more convenient to use the **partial pressures** (measured in atmospheres) of the substances. In this case, the equilibrium constant is K_p. For example, K_p for the Haber process is given by:

$$K_p = \frac{pNH_3^2}{pN_2 \times pH_2^3}$$

Tip When you write an equilibrium expression in terms of partial pressures, avoid all use of brackets (especially square ones).

You may be asked to give the units of the equilibrium constant. For the K_c expression above, the units are:
- mol^{2}dm^{-6} on the top line
- mol^{4}dm^{-12} on the bottom line

This cancels to give K_c the units of mol^{-2}dm^6.

For the K_p expression above, the units are:
- atm^2 on the top line
- atm^4 on the bottom line

Therefore, the units for K_p are atm^{-2}.

If the value of the equilibrium constant is very large, then the products predominate and the equilibrium lies over to the right-hand side. If the equilibrium constant is very small, then the reactants predominate and the equilibrium lies over to the left-hand side of the equation.

Heterogeneous equilibria

A **heterogeneous equilibrium** is one in which some of the substances are in different physical states. For example, in the thermal decomposition of calcium carbonate, calcium carbonate and calcium oxide are solids but carbon dioxide is a gas:

$$CaCO_3(s) \rightleftharpoons CaO(s) + CO_2(g)$$

If the thermal decomposition is carried out in a **closed system**, the carbon dioxide cannot escape and begins to react with the other product — calcium oxide — to reform calcium carbonate. At some point, equilibrium is obtained, i.e. calcium carbonate is being formed as fast as it is broken down.

For this reaction, the equilibrium expression for K_c is:

$$K_c = [CO_2(g)]_{eqm}$$

For K_p the equilibrium expression is:

$$K_p = pCO_2$$

The concentrations of the solids do not change and are not included in the expression.

Equilibrium and entropy

If ΔS_{total} for the forward reaction is positive, then ΔS_{total} for the reverse reaction is negative by the same amount. Therefore, for a reaction at equilibrium (the forward and the reverse reactions occur simultaneously and at the same rate), ΔS_{total} must equal zero.

Consider a reaction with a gaseous product, for example:

$$CaCO_3(s) \rightleftharpoons CaO(s) + CO_2(g)$$

Decreasing the pressure causes the volume to increase. Therefore, there are more ways of arranging the gas molecules. This means ΔS_{total} is increased, so the equilibrium shifts further to the right-hand side.

The forward reaction is endothermic ($\Delta H^{\ominus} = +178.3\,kJ\,mol^{-1}$).

In the reaction, 1 mole of solid produces 1 mole of another solid and 1 mole of gas. Therefore, the disorder increases (there are more ways of arranging the molecules), so ΔS_{system} is positive ($\Delta S_{system} = +160.4\,J\,mol^{-1}\,K^{-1}$).

$$\Delta S_{surroundings} = \frac{-(\Delta H)}{T}$$

At 298 K:

$$\Delta S_{surroundings} = \frac{-(+178.3) \times 1000}{298} = -598.3\,J\,mol^{-1}\,K^{-1}$$

$$\Delta S_{total} = +160.4 - 598.3 = -438\,J\,mol^{-1}\,K^{-1}$$

The negative sign means that the reaction is not spontaneous at 298 K.

At a higher temperature of 1500 K:
$$\Delta S_{surroundings} = -119\,J\,mol^{-1}\,K^{-1}$$
$$\Delta S_{total} = +41.4\,J\,mol^{-1}\,K^{-1}$$

The positive sign shows that at the higher temperature the reaction is spontaneous. So, raising the temperature turns this reaction from one that is not spontaneous to one which is spontaneous.

In other words, as the reaction is endothermic, raising the temperature favours the forward direction and the equilibrium moves to the right. Sounds familiar? Yes, this is Le Chatelier's principle explained in terms of entropy.

It is possible to calculate the temperature at which $\Delta S_{total} = 0.0\,J\,mol^{-1}\,K^{-1}$. For this to be the case, $\Delta S_{surroundings}$ must have the same value as ΔS_{system} but the opposite sign. So:

$$\frac{-(+178.3) \times 1000}{T} = -160.4$$

$$T = 1112\,K$$

At this temperature, the equilibrium constant $K_p = 1$.

Acid–base equilibria

Conjugate acid–base pairs

At AS, you learned that the Brønsted and Lowry definitions of acid–base behaviour are:
- An acid is a proton *donor*.
- A base is a proton *acceptor*.

$$H_2O(l) + HCl(g) \longrightarrow H_3O^+(aq) + Cl^-(aq)$$

The HCl has donated a proton and is, therefore, an acid; the water has accepted the proton and is, therefore, a base. The H_3O^+ ion formed is called the **oxonium ion**. This ion can also donate a proton, to form water again. Therefore, it too is an acid. It is the **conjugate acid** of water. The chloride ion is capable of accepting a proton and is, therefore, also a base. It is the **conjugate base** of HCl.
- The conjugate acid of a base is the product formed when a base accepts a proton.
- The conjugate base of an acid is the product formed when an acid donates a proton. For example:

$$NH_3(aq) + H_2O(l) \longrightarrow NH_4^+(aq) + OH^-(aq)$$
$$\text{base 1} \quad \text{acid 2} \qquad \text{acid 1} \qquad \text{base 2}$$

- $NH_3(aq)$ and $NH_4^+(aq)$ are a conjugate acid–base pair. $NH_4^+(aq)$ is the conjugate acid of $NH_3(aq)$.
- $H_2O(l)$ and $OH^-(aq)$ are also a conjugate acid–base pair. $H_2O(l)$ is the conjugate acid of $OH^-(aq)$.

The above reaction is a typical acid–base equilibrium composed of two acid–base conjugate pairs, with the bases competing for a proton.

Ionisation constant for water

Water ionises according to the following equilibrium:

$$H_2O(l) \rightleftharpoons H^+(aq) + OH^-(aq)$$

The equilibrium can be represented by an expression in which the equilibrium constant is known as K_w. The proportion of water molecules that ionises is very small, so the concentration of $H_2O(l)$ stays constant. This means it can be ignored.

$$K_w = [H^+(aq)][OH^-(aq)]$$

At 298 K:

$$K_w = 1 \times 10^{-14}\, mol^2\, dm^{-6}$$

In water or a neutral solution:

$$[H^+(aq)] = [OH^-(aq)]$$

Therefore:

$$[H^+(aq)] = \sqrt{(1 \times 10^{-14})}$$

So:

$$[H^+(aq)] = 1 \times 10^{-7}\, mol\, dm^{-3}$$

pH

We know that:

- the pH scale range is from 0 to 14
- pH of 7 is neutral
- a pH above 7 is alkaline
- a pH below 7 is acidic

The pH scale is logarithmic. This means, for example, that a solution of pH 3 is ten times more acidic than a solution of pH 4.

$$pH = -\log_{10}[H^+(aq)]$$

Tip You must learn this equation and always quote it in unit test answers on pH. There is often a mark simply for writing it down. You must also know how to use both the $\log_{10}$ and antilog$_{10}$/10^x buttons on your calculators.

It was shown above that for water:

$$[H^+(aq)] = 1 \times 10^{-7}\, mol\, dm^{-3}$$

Therefore:

$$pH = -\log_{10}(1 \times 10^{-7}) = 7$$

This proves what we have always known — pure water or a neutral solution has a pH of 7.

Finding the pH of a strong acid is straightforward. Simply find the negative log to the base 10 of the hydrogen ion concentration using your calculator. For example, $0.01 \, mol \, dm^{-3}$ H^+ has a pH of 2.

Finding the pH of an alkaline solution is trickier. We have to use:

$$K_w = [H^+(aq)][OH^-(aq)] = 1 \times 10^{-14} \, mol^2 \, dm^{-6}$$

For example, $0.01 \, mol \, dm^{-3}$ NaOH contains $0.01 \, mol \, dm^{-3}$ OH^-. This value is substituted into the expression for K_w so that we can find the hydrogen ion concentration:

$$[H^+(aq)] \times 0.01 = 1 \times 10^{-14} = 1 \times 10^{-12} \, mol \, dm^{-3}$$
$$pH = -\log_{10}(1 \times 10^{-12})$$
$$pH = 12$$

Tip Practise these calculations so you become familiar with them. They are very common on Unit Test 4.

Strong and weak acids and bases

You will have met this concept at AS.

A strong acid is one that ionises completely. Every molecule of HCl in dilute hydrochloric acid has split up into H^+ ions and Cl^- ions. So, in $0.1 \, mol \, dm^{-3}$ HCl the concentration of hydrogen ions is $0.1 \, mol \, dm^{-3}$.

Strong bases (e.g. NaOH) are also completely ionised in solution.

With strong acids and bases the acid–base equilibria are right over to the right-hand side.

A weak acid (or base) is only *slightly* ionised. Nearly all organic acids (e.g. ethanoic acid) are weak.

Tip For the unit test, learn this definition of a weak acid. The magic word is 'slightly'.

For a weak acid, for example, the equilibrium is:

$$HA(aq) \rightleftharpoons H^+(aq) + A^-(aq)$$

In the equilibrium expression, the equilibrium constant is K_a — the dissociation constant of the acid.

$$K_a = \frac{[H^+(aq)][A^-(aq)]}{[HA(aq)]}$$

To find the pH of a weak acid, the concentration of the acid and its K_a value must be known. Suppose we need to find the pH of a $0.01 \, mol \, dm^{-3}$ solution of ethanoic acid ($K_a = 1.7 \times 10^{-5} \, mol^2 \, dm^{-6}$):

$$HA(aq) \rightleftharpoons H^+(aq) + A^-(aq)$$

	HA(aq)	H$^+$(aq)	A$^-$(aq)
Initial concentration	0.01	nil	nil
Concentration at equilibrium	$0.01 - x$	x	x

Every time an HA molecule ionises, one H^+ ion and one A^- ion are produced. Therefore:

$[H^+(aq)] = [A^-(aq)] = x$

$$K_a = 1.7 \times 10^{-5} = \frac{x^2}{0.01 - x}$$

Carrying on with the calculation in this manner would lead to a quadratic equation, which it is better to avoid. So, an approximation is made.

It is assumed that the equilibrium concentration of the undissociated acid is the same as the initial concentration, because the degree of dissociation is slight. This assumption avoids the quadratic equation. It is also assumed that any hydrogen ions produced by the ionisation of water can be ignored.

The simplified equation is:

$1.7 \times 10^{-5} \times 0.01 = x^2$

Therefore:

$$x = \sqrt{(1.7 \times 10^{-5} \times 0.01)}$$
$$x = 4.1 \times 10^{-4}\,mol\,dm^{-3}$$
$$pH = -\log_{10}(4.1 \times 10^{-4}) = 3.4$$

Note: express pH values to 2 significant figures only.

Tip If asked in the unit test to state what assumptions you have made you should write: 'The concentration of hydrogen ions (x) is going to be very small, so $(0.01 - x) \approx 0.01$.'

HCl of the same concentration would be pH 2, because it is a strong acid.

Acid–base titration curves

In the unit test, you might be asked to do a calculation similar to the one above, to find the pH of a weak acid. You might then be asked to sketch the pH curve produced when a certain volume of this acid is titrated with excess base of the same concentration. A set of axes will usually be provided on the question paper.

Tip Accuracy will be expected.

The curve will begin at the pH you have calculated.

Tip If the question is about adding acid to alkali, then the graph will start at an alkaline pH. If the question is about adding alkali to acid, then the graph will start at an acidic pH. Be aware of this.

Weak acid–strong base titration

For a weak acid titrated with a strong base, the graph slopes gently upwards to just under pH 7. This is the region of the graph where the solution is acting as a buffer (pp. 42–43).

Just below pH 7, there is a sharp and dramatic rise to between pH 10 and 11. The graph then curves off to a horizontal line above pH 11. The midpoint of the sharp rise should occur at between pH 8 and 9 and should be at the same volume as the volume of acid used.

The graph below, of pH against volume of base added, is the titration curve obtained when $40\,cm^3\,0.01\,mol\,dm^{-3}$ NaOH is added to $25\,cm^3$ of $0.01\,mol\,dm^{-3}$ ethanoic acid.

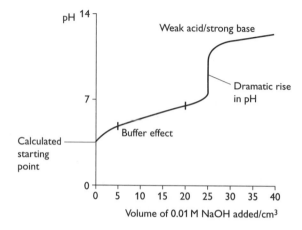

The indicator used in this titration is phenolphthalein because the colour change of this indicator occurs at a pH on the vertical part of the graph. In a weak acid–strong base titration the exact end point is at an alkaline pH. In this case, the product is sodium ethanoate.

Tip You could be told that the pH of a solution of a salt (e.g. sodium ethanoate) is alkaline and asked to explain why. It is alkaline because sodium ethanoate is a salt made from a *weak* acid and a *strong* base.

Strong acid–strong base titration

The graph below is the titration curve obtained when $40\,cm^3\,0.01\,mol\,dm^{-3}$ NaOH is added to $25\,cm^3$ of $0.01\,mol\,dm^{-3}$ solution of a strong acid, such as HCl.

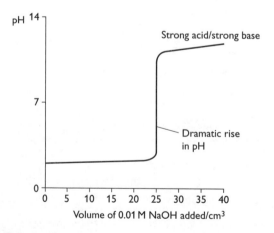

Strong acid–weak base titration

The graph below is the titration curve obtained when $40\,cm^3\,0.01\,mol\,dm^{-3}$ NH_3 is added to $25\,cm^3$ of $0.01\,mol\,dm^{-3}$ solution of a strong acid, such as HCl.

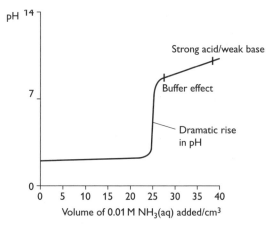

Volume of 0.01 M NH₃(aq) added/cm³

Weak acid–weak base titration

The graph below is the titration curve obtained when $40\ \text{cm}^3$ $0.01\ \text{mol dm}^{-3}$ NH_3 is added to $25\ \text{cm}^3$ of $0.01\ \text{mol dm}^{-3}$ solution of a weak acid, such as ethanoic acid.

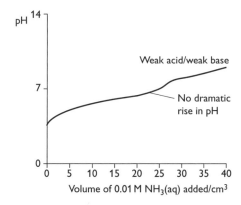

Volume of 0.01 M NH₃(aq) added/cm³

Indicators

The correct choice of indicator for a titration is very important. It is decided by the extent and range of pH values over which the dramatic increase in pH occurs (the 'vertical' portion of the titration curve).

Type of titration	Example of acid and base used	pH range of vertical part of graph	Indicator
Strong acid–strong base	HCl and NaOH	3 to 10	Any
Weak acid–strong base	Ethanoic acid and NaOH	7 to 10	Phenolphthalein
Strong acid–weak base	HCl and ammonia solution	3 to 7	Screened methyl orange
Weak acid–weak base	Ethanoic acid and ammonia	No vertical part to graph	None suitable

Tip You should learn the colour changes of two indicators and make sure that you can describe the colour changes the right way round. For example, if asked to describe the colour change at the end point of a titration in which NaOH is added to HCl with phenolphthalein as the indicator, it would be wrong to describe the colour change as being from pink to colourless. It would actually be from colourless to pink.

Indicator	Colour in acid	Colour in alkali
Phenolphthalein	Colourless	Pink
Screened methyl orange	Purple	Green

Indicators are weak acids in which the acid form is a different colour to its conjugate base. They are complex molecules, so the formula HInd is used to represent them.

$$HInd(aq) \rightleftharpoons H^+(aq) + Ind^-(aq)$$
    Colour 1   Colour 2

When acid is added, the indicator equilibrium moves to the left-hand side and colour 1 predominates. Addition of base (such as OH^-) removes the H^+ ions. This causes the indicator equilibrium to move to the right-hand side and so colour 2 predominates. Therefore, the colour of the indicator depends on the pH.

Buffer solutions

A buffer solution is one that resists a change in pH on addition of *small* amounts of acid or alkali.

Tip You should know how to define a buffer solution.

A buffer consists of a weak acid and its conjugate base, or a weak base and its conjugate acid. For example:
- $0.1 \, mol \, dm^{-3}$ ethanoic acid mixed with $0.1 \, mol \, dm^{-3}$ ethanoate ions (from sodium ethanoate)
- $0.1 \, mol \, dm^{-3}$ ammonia solution mixed with $0.1 \, mol \, dm^{-3}$ ammonium ions (from ammonium chloride)

Tip You need to know these two buffer systems at least and to be able to recognise others.

In the ethanoic acid–sodium ethanoate buffer system the following equilibrium exists:
$$CH_3COOH(aq) \rightleftharpoons CH_3COO^-(aq) + H^+(aq)$$

This buffer is effective over a pH range of approximately 3.8 to 5.3. It is $0.1 \, mol \, dm^{-3}$ with respect to both the acid and the ethanoate ions.

When a small amount of acid is added, the H^+ ions react with the ethanoate ions. The equilibrium shifts to the left-hand side to form undissociated ethanoic acid. The extra H^+ ions are, therefore, removed and the pH remains almost constant.

When a small amount of alkali is added, the OH^- ions react with the H^+ ions present to form water:
$$H^+(aq) + OH^-(aq) \longrightarrow H_2O(l)$$

content guidance

The ethanoic acid equilibrium moves to the right-hand side to replace these lost H^+ ions and the pH remains unchanged.

You may be asked to perform calculations on buffer solutions. You will always be provided with the necessary equation:

$$pH = -\log_{10} K_a - \log_{10}([acid]/[base])$$

In the example of the ethanoic acid buffer above, [acid] = [base] = $0.1 \, mol \, dm^{-3}$, so $pH = -\log_{10} K_a$. Since $K_a = 1.7 \times 10^{-5} \, mol \, dm^{-3}$, pH = 4.8.

The formula can be used to work out the volumes to be mixed to form a buffer.

Example

What volumes of 0.1 mol dm^{-3} ethanoic acid and 0.1 mol dm^{-3} sodium ethanoate should be mixed to form 1 dm^3 of a buffer solution of pH 5.3?

$$pH = -\log_{10} K_a - \log_{10}([acid]/[base])$$
$$5.3 = -\log_{10}(1.7 \times 10^{-5}) - \log_{10}([acid]/[base])$$
$$5.3 - 4.8 = -(\log_{10}[acid]/[base])$$
$$[acid]/[base] = antilog_{10}(-0.5)$$
$$[acid]/[base] = 0.32$$

This is the same as saying that the ratio of the volumes of acid to base is 0.32:1. The 1 dm^3 of solution has to be divided in the same ratio.

To find the volume, x, of 0.1 mol dm^{-3} ethanoic acid:

$$\frac{0.32}{1.32} = \frac{\text{volume of acid}}{\text{total volume}} = \frac{x}{1000}$$

so

$$x = \frac{320}{1.32} = 242 \, cm^3 \text{ of ethanoic acid}$$

The volume of 0.1 mol dm^{-3} sodium ethanoate is 1000 – 242 = 758 cm^3

Mixing together 242 cm^3 of ethanoic acid with 758 cm^3 sodium ethanoate would give a buffer solution of the required pH.

Oxidation products of alcohols

Carbonyl compounds

The carbonyl group is a carbon atom double bonded to an oxygen atom:

C=O

There are two types of compound that contain a carbonyl group as the only functional group — **aldehydes** and **ketones**.

You will have met aldehydes and ketones before because they are the products of the oxidation of alcohols (using a mixture of sulphuric acid and potassium dichromate):

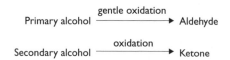

- Aldehydes have an alkyl group and a hydrogen atom bonded to the carbonyl carbon atom. Aldehydes can be oxidised further to carboxylic acids.
- Ketones have two alkyl groups attached to the carbonyl carbon atom. Ketones cannot be oxidised further.

The aldehyde and ketone shown below are isomers. They have the same molecular formula, C_3H_6O.

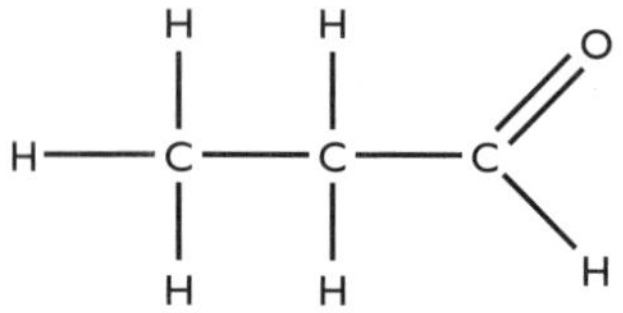

CH_3CH_2CHO
Propanal

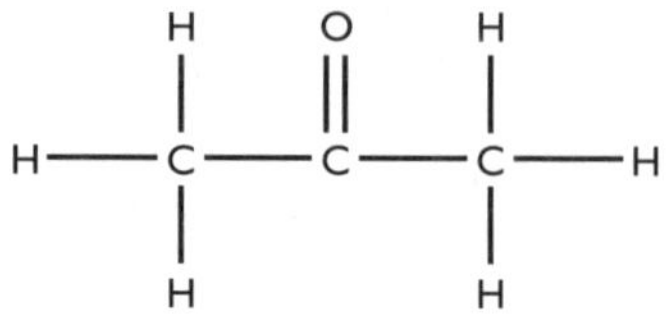

CH_3COCH_3
Propanone

Tip The correct name of the ketone of molecular formula C_4H_8O is butanone, *not* butan-2-one — the carbonyl group can be on the second carbon atom only.

Oxygen is a very electronegative atom, so the carbonyl group has a dipole:

$C^{\delta+} = O^{\delta-}$

This means that carbonyl compounds are susceptible to attack by nucleophiles:

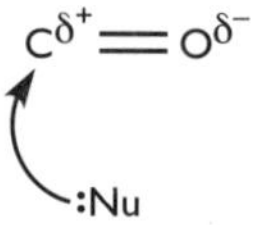

$C^{\delta+} = O^{\delta-}$

:Nu

Tip Remember that a nucleophile is a species with a pair of electrons available to form a new covalent bond.

Reactions of carbonyl compounds
Solubility
Aldehydes and ketones are soluble in water because they form hydrogen bonds with water molecules.

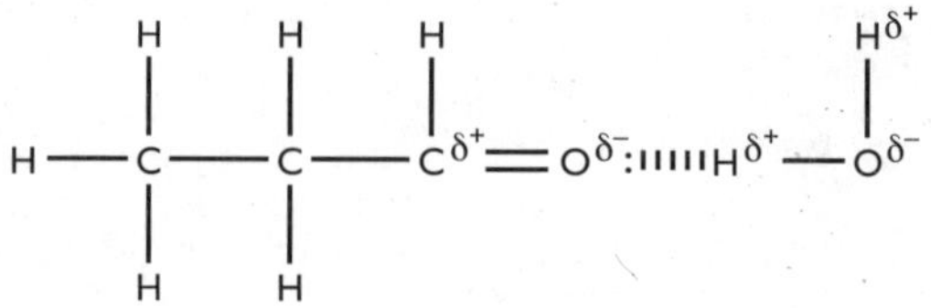

As the size of the alkyl group increases, the solubility decreases.

Combustion

Aldehydes and ketones undergo complete combustion to form carbon dioxide and water.

Reaction with Brady's reagent (2,4-dinitrophenylhydrazine)

All aldehydes and ketones react with Brady's reagent (a deep-orange solution) to form yellow/orange crystalline precipitates. The reaction is used as a test for aldehydes and ketones. It is a **nucleophilic** reaction that is also called an addition–elimination reaction.

Ethanal   2,4-dinitrophenylhydrazine

Ethanal 2,4-dinitrophenylhydrazone

The solid product can be recrystallised from a *minimum volume of hot solvent* and the melting point found. The original aldehyde or ketone can then be identified by comparing the melting point with values given in the literature.

Tip You do not need to learn the mechanism of this reaction.

Tests for aldehydes and ketones

Aldehydes can be oxidised to carboxylic acids:

$$CH_3CHO \longrightarrow CH_3COOH$$

Ketones cannot be oxidised.

This can be used to differentiate between an aldehyde and a ketone. The two reactions used are summarised in the table below.

Reaction	Result with aldehydes	Result with ketones
Reflux with potassium dichromate and sulphuric acid	Orange solution turns green/blue	Stays orange
Warm with Benedict's solution	Blue solution forms red precipitate	Stays blue

The red precipitate formed in a positive Benedict's test is copper(I) oxide, Cu_2O.

Tip When describing a negative result *never* write the word 'nothing'. A description of the colour is a much better answer than 'no reaction'.

Carboxylic acids

The functional group of a carboxylic acid is the carboxyl group. This consists of a carbonyl group and an –OH group attached to the carbonyl carbon atom. The formula of ethanoic acid is:

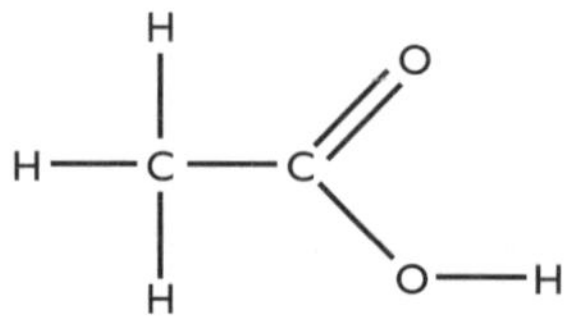

As described earlier (pp. 38–39), carboxylic acids are weak acids, i.e. they are only slightly ionised in water:

$$CH_3COOH + H_2O \rightleftharpoons CH_3COO^- + H_3O^+$$

This happens because the carboxylate anion (in this case ethanoate) is slightly stabilised by delocalisation and can therefore exist:

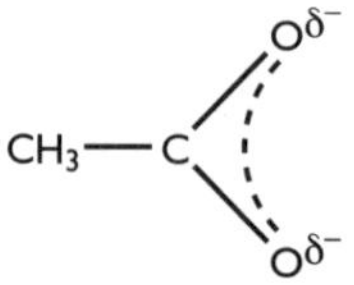

Reactions of carboxylic acids
Solubility
As with alcohols, aldehydes and ketones, carboxylic acids are soluble in water because of their ability to form hydrogen bonds:

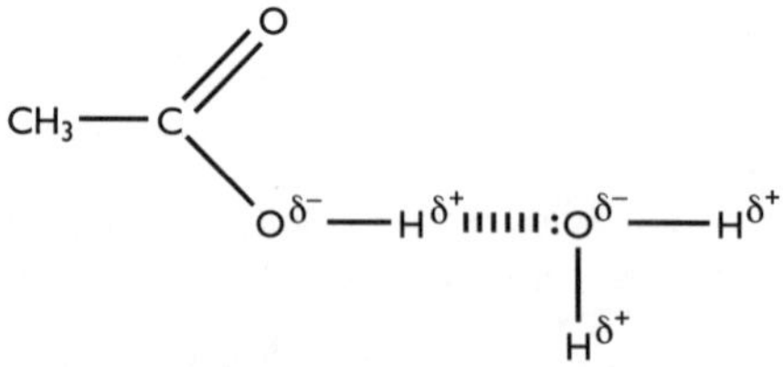

The solutions are acidic; $0.1 \, mol \, dm^{-3}$ ethanoic acid has a pH of 3.

Formation of salts
As with all acids, carboxylic acids react with:
- metals to form a salt and hydrogen
$$2CH_3COOH + 2Na \longrightarrow 2CH_3COO^-Na^+ + H_2$$
sodium ethanoate

- bases to form salt and water

$$CH_3COOH + NaOH \longrightarrow CH_3COO^-Na^+ + H_2O$$

- carbonates to form salts, liberating carbon dioxide

$$2CH_3COOH + Na_2CO_3 \longrightarrow 2CH_3COO^-Na^+ + CO_2 + H_2O$$

Ester formation

Carboxylic acids react with alcohols to form esters. For example:

$$CH_3COOH + C_2H_5OH \rightleftharpoons CH_3COOC_2H_5 + H_2O$$
$$\text{ethyl ethanoate}$$

Tip This is an equilibrium reaction that requires H^+ ions (provided by sulphuric acid) as a catalyst.

Esterification involves **nucleophilic** attack. The lone pair of electrons on the oxygen atom of the alcohol is attracted to the δ^+ charge on the carbon atom of the carboxylic acid group:

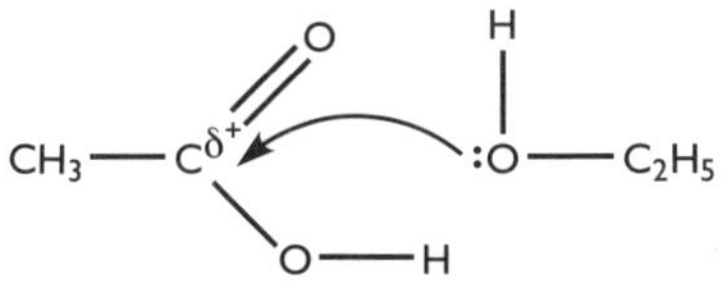

Usually, it is the O–H bond in the acid group that breaks. Unusually, it is the C–O bond in the carboxylic acid group that breaks.

Tip It is quite difficult to name esters. To name an ester, remember that the alcohol part comes first and the part derived from the acid second.

Alcohol	Acid	Ester
Methanol	Propanoic acid	Methyl propanoate
Propan-1-ol	Methanoic acid	Propyl methanoate
Ethanol	Benzoic acid	Ethyl benzoate
Butan-1-ol	Ethanoic acid	Butyl ethanoate

Reduction

Carboxylic acids can be reduced to the corresponding *primary* alcohol using the powerful reducing agent lithium aluminium hydride (lithium tetrahydridoaluminate(III), $LiAlH_4$). For example:

$$CH_3COOH \xrightarrow{LiAlH_4} C_2H_5OH$$

This also involves nucleophilic attack, the nucleophile being the H^- ion.

Tip Lithium aluminium hydride will also reduce the following:
- an aldehyde to a primary alcohol
- a ketone to a secondary alcohol

Carboxylic acid derivatives

You need to be able to name and write out formulae for esters and acyl chlorides.

Methyl benzoate, $CH_3OOCC_6H_5$, is an example of an ester:

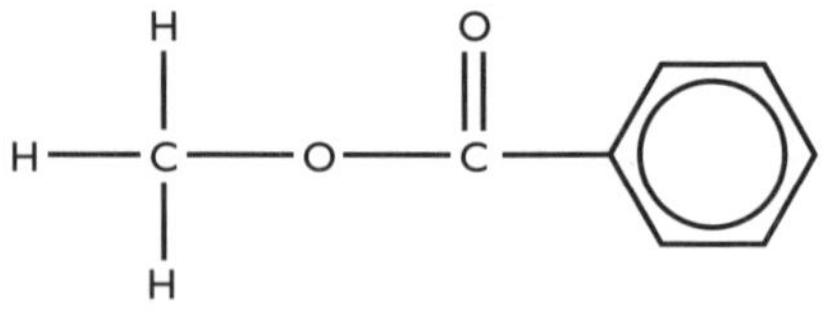

Ethanoyl chloride, CH_3COCl, is an example of an acyl chloride:

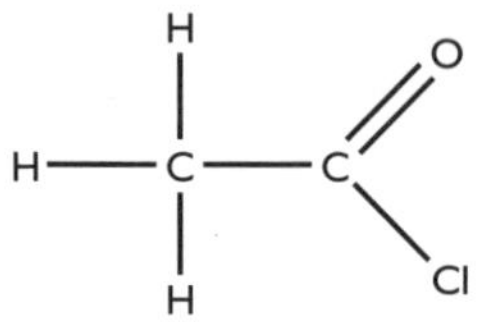

Esters

Esters hydrolyse slowly in water but more rapidly if dilute acid or base is added as a catalyst. This is another nucleophilic reaction. The lone pair of electrons on the oxygen atom of the water or the oxygen atom of the OH^- group from the base attacks the carbon in the carboxyl group.

If an acid catalyst is used, an equilibrium is set up and the corresponding carboxylic acid and alcohol are produced:

$$CH_3COOC_2H_5 + H_2O \overset{H^+}{\rightleftharpoons} CH_3COOH + C_2H_5OH$$
ethyl ethanoate

This is the reverse of the ester formation reaction described above.

If a base such as sodium hydroxide is used as the catalyst, the product is the carboxylate anion, rather than the acid:

$$CH_3COOC_2H_5 + OH^- \longrightarrow CH_3COO^- + C_2H_5OH$$

Esters are used as fragrances in perfumes and as food flavourings.

Tip Examiners often refer to esters as 'sweet-smelling liquids'.

Acyl chlorides

An acyl chloride can be thought of as the compound formed when the –OH group of a carboxylic acid is replaced by a chlorine atom.

Acyl chlorides are very reactive. They react vigorously with nucleophiles such as water and alcohols.

The presence of two very electronegative atoms (oxygen and chlorine) attached to the carbonyl carbon makes the δ^+ on that carbon *much larger* than in the carboxylic acid and, therefore, *more attractive* to nucleophiles:

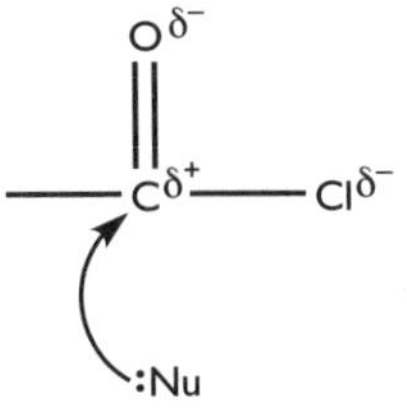

Nucleophilic attack by water on an acyl chloride (hydrolysis) produces the carboxylic acid and hydrogen chloride gas. For example:

$$CH_3COCl + H_2O \longrightarrow CH_3COOH + HCl$$

Nucleophilic attack of an alcohol on an acyl chloride produces an ester and hydrogen chloride gas:

$$CH_3COCl + C_2H_5OH \longrightarrow CH_3COOC_2H_5 + HCl$$

This is a good way of making an ester because, unlike using a carboxylic acid, the reaction goes to completion and there is no need for a catalyst.

Infrared spectra

Questions asked about the interpretation of infrared spectra tend to be very straightforward.

Absorption wavenumber range/cm⁻¹	Group
1740–1720	C=O stretching in aldehydes
1700–1680	C=O stretching in ketones
2900–2820 and 2775–2700	C–H stretching in aldehydes
3300–2500	O–H stretching in carboxylic acids

- The absorption due to the O–H stretching in carboxylic acids is very broad because of hydrogen bonding.
- Absorption is due to individual bonds between atoms (e.g. O–H, C=O, C–O) and is *not* due to groups of atoms found in functional groups (e.g.–CHO, –COOH).

Tip You need to be very specific in your answers about which bond you are referring to. For example, the absorption by the C–H bond in the aldehyde functional group is at a different wavenumber to the absorption by a C–H bond in an alkyl group (e.g. –CH₃). Therefore, this can be used to distinguish between an aldehyde and a ketone. The ketone will not have the absorption due to an aldehyde C–H.

Questions
&
Answers

In this section of the guide, there are five questions which between them test all the requirements of the Unit 4 specification. They represent the kinds of questions you will get in the unit test. In contrast to the real thing, there are no lines or spaces left for the answers. Instead, the presence of a space or number of lines is indicated. The number of marks is, of course, also shown. However, taken together, these questions are much longer than a single paper, so do not try to do them all in 90 minutes.

After each question, you will find the answers of two candidates — Candidate A and Candidate B (using different candidates for each question). In each case, Candidate A is performing at the C/D level, while Candidate B is an A-grade candidate.

Examiner's comments

All candidate responses are followed by examiner's comments. These are preceded by the icon e and indicate where credit is due. In the weaker answers, they also point out areas for improvement, specific problems and common errors.

How to use this section

- Do the question, giving yourself a time limit of $1\frac{1}{2}$ minutes per mark; do not look at the candidates' answers or examiner's comments before you attempt the question yourself.
- Compare your answers with the candidates' answers and decide what the correct answer is; still do not look at the examiner's comments while doing this.
- Finally, look at the examiner's comments.

Completing this section will teach you a lot of chemistry and vastly improve your exam technique.

Rates of reaction

This question is about the reaction of 1-bromobutane with sodium hydroxide:

$$C_4H_9Br + NaOH \longrightarrow C_4H_9OH + NaBr$$

0.250 moles of 1-bromobutane and 0.250 moles of sodium hydroxide were mixed in ethanol at a certain temperature. The concentration of hydroxide ions was determined at various times, as shown in the table below.

Time/h	$[OH^-]$/mol dm^{-3}
0	0.25
1.0	0.21
2.5	0.17
5.0	0.135
7.5	0.11
10.0	0.095
15.0	0.07
20.0	0.06
25.0	0.055

(a) Suggest a method of 'following' this reaction. (*3 lines*) (2 marks)

(b) Suggest why ethanol, not water, is used as the solvent. (*2 lines*) (1 mark)

(c) (i) On graph paper, plot a graph of concentration of OH$^-$ (vertical axis) against time (horizontal axis). (2 marks)

(ii) Measure two successive half-lives for the reaction, showing these on the graph. (2 marks)

(iii) Give the order of reaction and explain how you deduced this from these two successive half-lives. (*1 line*) (2 marks)

(d) The order in (c) (iii) is the overall order of the reaction. To find the order with respect to C_4H_9Br, another procedure was followed. This involved measuring the initial rate of reaction in two experiments. The results are shown below.

Initial concentration of C_4H_9Br/mol dm^{-3}	Initial concentration of NaOH/mol dm^{-3}	Initial rate of reaction/mol dm^{-3} s^{-1}
0.25	0.20	6.4×10^{-6}
0.50	0.20	1.3×10^{-5}

(i) Calculate the order of reaction with respect to C_4H_9Br, explaining your method. (*3 lines*) (2 marks)

(ii) Write the rate equation for the reaction. (*space*) (1 mark)

(iii) Use the results in the table to calculate a value for the *rate constant* for this reaction and give its units. (*space*) (2 marks)

(iv) An isomer of 1-bromobutane reacts with hydroxide ions in a reaction that is zero order with respect to hydroxide. Suggest the *rate-determining step* of the reaction. (*space*) (1 mark)

(e) A student set out to measure the activation energy of a reaction by measuring the rate constant at various temperatures. She then used the Arrhenius equation:

$$\ln \text{rate} = \ln A - E_A/RT$$

to plot a suitable graph and calculate the value of the activation energy, E_A. Explain how she did this. (*4 lines*) (2 marks)

(f) The diagram below shows the distribution of energy in a sample of molecules that react together.

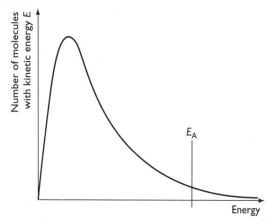

(i) Mark on the graph the activation energy for the same reaction with a catalyst present. Label this E_c. (1 mark)

(ii) Draw a line showing the distribution of energies at a higher temperature. (1 mark)

Total: 19 marks

■ ■ ■

Candidates' answers to Question 1

Candidate A

(a) Titrate with standard hydrochloric acid.

Candidate B

(a) Withdraw a sample of known volume and titrate with hydrochloric acid of known concentration.

   Both candidates are on the right track. However, Candidate A implies that the whole volume should be titrated, rather than a sample, so he only scores 1 mark for titrating with hydrochloric acid. Candidate B gains both marks.

Candidate A

(b) Bromobutane does not dissolve in water.

Candidate B

(b) Both sodium hydroxide and bromobutane are soluble in ethanol.

e Both candidates score the mark. Candidate B is wise to mention the sodium hydroxide as well, although it is not essential here.

Candidate A

(c) (i) and (c) (ii)

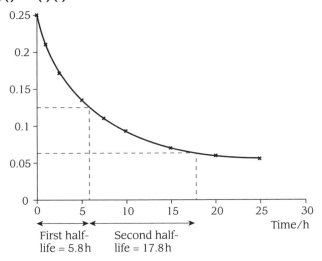

First half-
life = 5.8h

Second half-
life = 17.8h

Candidate B

(c) (i) and (c) (ii)

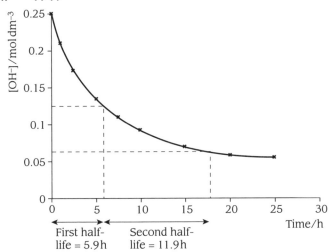

First half-
life = 5.9h

Second half-
life = 11.9h

e In plotting graphs, 1 mark is given for labelled axes, including units and a sensible scale. Candidate A has failed to label the *y*-axis, which loses him the mark. Candidate B scores this mark. Both candidates score the second mark, which is for correctly plotting the points and drawing a smooth curve through them.

Candidate A identifies the first half-life correctly. However, he makes the common error of measuring the second half-life from the origin, not from the end of the first half-life, so he scores only 1 of the 2 marks available. Candidate B gains both marks.

Candidate A

(c) (iii) Second order

Candidate B

(c) (iii) Second order, since the half-life is not constant.

 Both candidates score the mark for the order. Candidate A has forgotten to justify his answer, so he does not score the second mark. Candidate B has given a correct justification and scores both marks.

Candidate A

(d) (i) When you double the concentration of bromobutane at constant hydroxide concentration, the rate doubles, so it's first order.

Candidate B

(d) (i) The reaction is first order with respect to 1-bromobutane. When the concentration of bromobutane is doubled from 0.25 to 0.50, the rate doubles from 6.4×10^{-6} to 1.3×10^{-5}. Thus, concentration is proportional to rate.

 Candidate B has written a very full answer but she has omitted to say that the concentration of hydroxide ions remains constant in the two experiments, so she loses a mark and gains only 1 out of 2 marks. Candidate A's answer is much briefer, but he makes both points sufficiently well to score 2 marks.

Candidate A

(d) (ii) Rate = $k[C_4H_9Br]$

Candidate B

(d) (ii) Rate = $k[C_4H_9Br][OH^-]$

 Candidate A has not deduced that, if the overall order is second and the reaction is first order with respect to 1-bromobutane, it must also be first with respect to OH^-. He fails to score. Candidate B is correct and scores the mark.

Candidate A

(d) (iii) $k = \dfrac{6.4 \times 10^{-6}}{0.25} = 2.56 \times 10^{-5}\,s^{-1}$

Candidate B

(d) (iii) $\dfrac{1.3 \times 10^{-5}}{0.5 \times 0.2} = 1.3 \times 10^{-4}\,dm^3\,mol^{-1}\,s^{-1}$

 Candidate A's answer is incorrect, because it is based on the wrong rate equation. However, it scores the 2 marks, by 'transferred error'. Candidate B has the correct answer and the correct units and scores 2 marks.

Candidate A

(d) (iv) RBr + OH⁻ $\longrightarrow$ ROH + Br⁻

Candidate B

(d) (iv) RBr $\longrightarrow$ R⁺ + Br⁻

R⁺ + OH⁻ $\longrightarrow$ ROH

e Neither candidate scores! Candidate A has given the equation for the reaction that is first order with respect to both RBr and OH⁻. This is the case for the 1-bromobutane reaction — however, we are now talking about the reaction of the isomer 2-bromo-2-methylpropane. Candidate B would have scored if she had stopped after her first equation. She has given the whole mechanism (correctly) but she has not answered the question, which asked for the *rate-determining* (i.e. slowest) *step*.

Candidate A

(e) Plot a graph of ln(rate) against $1/T$. The slope will be E_A/R from which, knowing the value of R, E_A can be calculated.

Candidate B

(e) Plot a graph of ln(rate) on the *x*-axis against $1/T$. Measure the slope ($\Delta y/\Delta x$). This will equal $-E_A/R$.

e Candidate A scores 1 mark for what to plot on the graph. However, he has not stated what to plot on which axis, which is sailing close to the wind. He does not score the second mark because he leaves out the minus sign before E_A/R. This is a pity as otherwise the second part of his answer is good and well constructed. Candidate B just scores 2 marks, though she could have done with Candidate A's ending ('knowing the value of R, E_A can be calculated') to make the logical steps.

Candidate A

(f) (i) and (f) (ii)

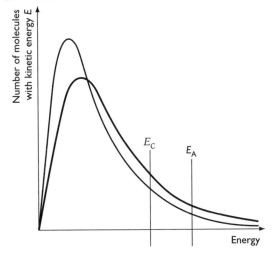

question

Candidate B

(f) (i) and (f) (ii)

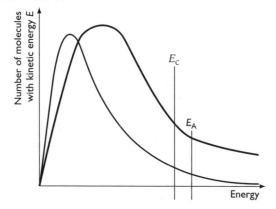

📝 Both candidates have correctly shown the lower activation energy for the catalysed route and score 1 mark. Candidate A has also shown the correct line for the higher temperature. The peak must be lower (as well as to the right of the original peak) because the total area under both curves must be equal — it represents the same number of molecules. Candidate B has not realised this and her graph goes too high. Candidate B does not score here, whereas Candidate A scores the second mark.

📝 **Overall, Candidate A scores 11 out of 19 marks. Candidate B scores 16.**

Reactions of salicylic acid

Some reactions of the compound 'salicylic acid' are shown below:

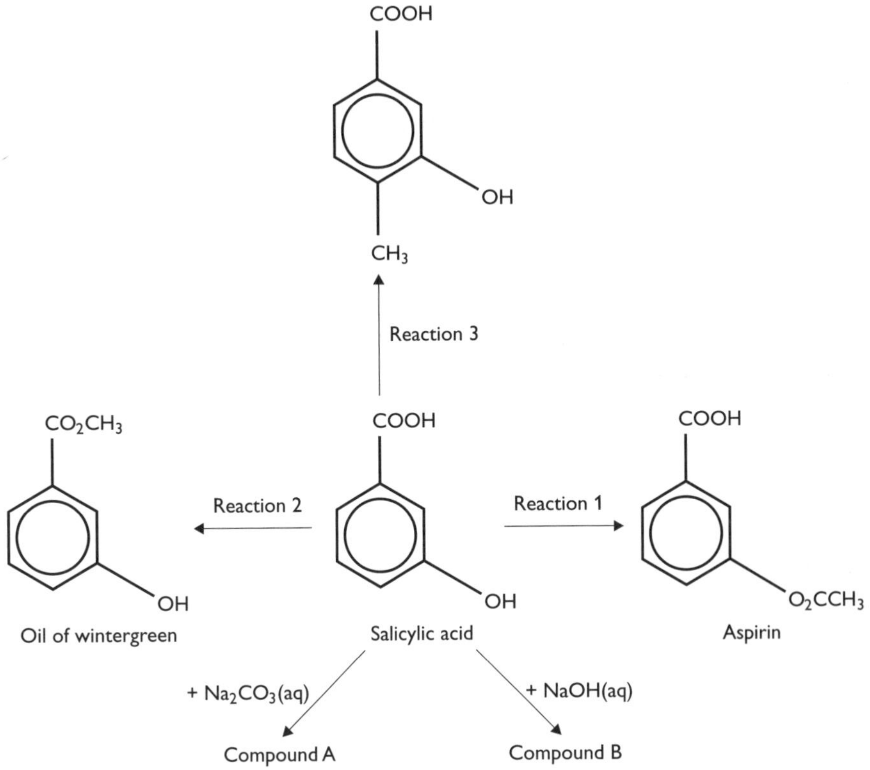

COOH

OH

CH$_3$

↑

Reaction 3

CO$_2$CH$_3$

Reaction 2

OH

Oil of wintergreen

COOH

OH

Salicylic acid

Reaction 1

COOH

O$_2$CCH$_3$

Aspirin

+ Na$_2$CO$_3$(aq)

Compound A

+ NaOH(aq)

Compound B

(a) Name the two functional groups attached to the benzene ring in salicylic acid. (*1 line*)   (2 marks)

(b) Name and draw the displayed formula of the functional group that aspirin and oil of wintergreen have in common. (*1 line, space*)   (2 marks)

(c) Suggest the reagent for reaction 1. (*1 line*)   (1 mark)

(d) Suggest the reagents and the conditions for reaction 2. (*2 lines*)   (2 marks)

(e) Suggest how aspirin can be turned back to salicylic acid. (*2 lines*)   (2 marks)

(f) (i) Draw the structural formulae of compound A and compound B. (*space*)   (2 marks)

    (ii) Explain why sodium carbonate and sodium hydroxide react differently with salicylic acid. (*2 lines*)   (1 mark)

    (iii) What bond is broken in the formation of compound A? (*1 line*)   (1 mark)

(g) (i) Give the reagents for reaction 3. (*1 line*)   (2 marks)

    (ii) Name the type of reaction and its mechanism. (*1 line*)   (2 marks)

(h) Draw the structural formula of a possible nitration product of salicylic acid. (*space*)   (1 mark)

Total: 18 marks

Candidates' answers to Question 2

Candidate A
(a) Acid and phenolic –OH

Candidate B
(a) Carboxylic acid and phenolic –OH

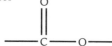 Candidate A scores 1 mark for phenolic –OH but she has not been specific enough in naming the other group. Candidate B scores both marks as he gives phenolic –OH and *carboxylic* acid.

Candidate A

(b) Ester

$$—COO—$$

Candidate B

(b) Ester

$$—C\overset{\displaystyle O}{\overset{\|}{}}—O—$$

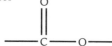 Candidate A scores 1 mark for 'ester'. She clearly knows how the formula is arranged but fails to score the second mark because she does not follow the instructions to display the formula fully. Candidate B is correct and scores both marks.

Candidate A
(c) Ethanoyl chloride

Candidate B
(c) Ethanoic anhydride

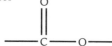 Both candidates score the mark as either of these reagents will work given the right conditions. The reagent to avoid is ethanoic acid, which does not react with phenols.

Candidate A
(d) Methanol, reflux

Candidate B
(d) Methanol and sulphuric acid

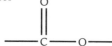 Both candidates score 1 mark for the reagent but fail to score for the conditions. Candidate A leaves out the sulphuric acid and Candidate B leaves out the need to heat under reflux.

Candidate A
(e) Heat aspirin with sodium hydroxide.

Candidate B
(e) Heat aspirin with dilute hydrochloric acid.

🖉 Candidate A scores 1 of the 2 marks available. Sodium hydroxide does catalyse the hydrolysis of an ester but the *salt* of the acid is formed. Candidate B is correct and scores 2 marks. Hydrochloric acid catalyses the hydrolysis of an ester to produce the acid itself and the alcohol.

Candidate A

(f) (i)

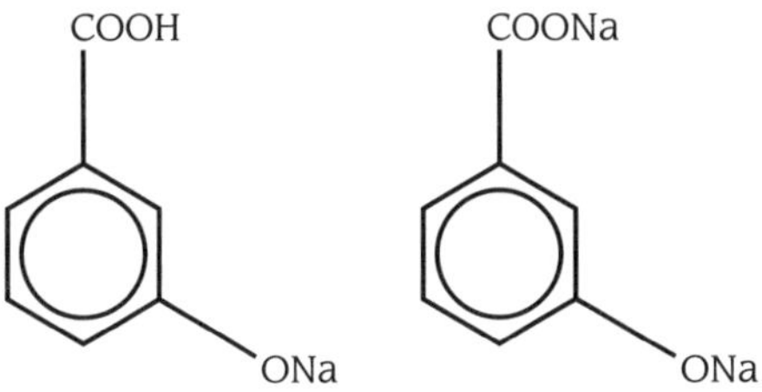

COOH   COONa

ONa   ONa

Candidate B

(f) (i)

C—O—Na   C—O—Na

O—H   O—Na

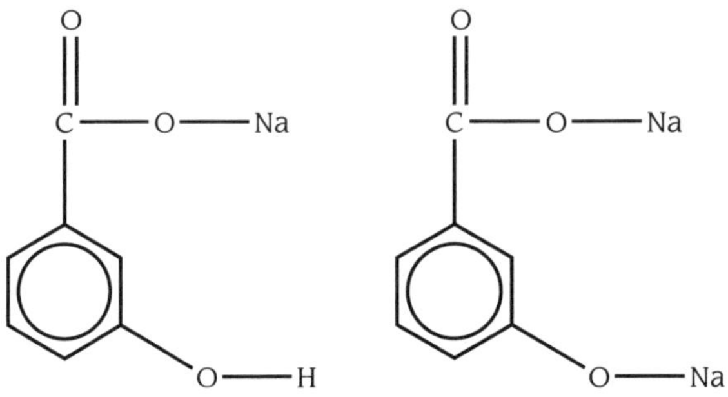

🖉 Both candidates score 1 mark. Candidate A has compound B correct but it would have been sensible to label it. However, unless otherwise stated, the examiner would assume that the second formula given was compound B. It is also best (but not essential) to show the compounds as ionic, i.e. COO^-Na^+ and O^-Na^+. The formula given by Candidate A for compound A is incorrect. It is the carboxylic acid, not the phenolic –OH group, that reacts with sodium carbonate. Candidate B has the compounds correct but, by trying to give too much detail, he has fallen into error. These compounds are ionic, *not* covalent.

Candidate A

(f) (ii) Carboxylic acids do not react with carbonates.

Candidate B

(f) (ii) Phenols are weaker acids than carboxylic acids

🖉 Candidate A is consistent with her error from (f) (i). However, she does not score because her answer is not an explanation, merely a statement of what she thinks happens. Candidate B has given the correct explanation and scores the mark.

Candidate A

(f) (iii) OH

Candidate B

(f) (iii) O–H

e Candidate B's answer is better, but both candidates score the mark.

Candidate A

(g) (i) Aluminium chloride and methanol

Candidate B

(g) (i) $AlCl_3$ and CH_3Cl

e Candidate B has the correct reagents and scores 2 marks. Candidate A scores 1 mark for aluminium chloride but does not score for methanol.

Candidate A

(g) (ii) Electrophilic addition

Candidate B

(g) (ii) Electrophilic substitution

e Candidate A scores 1 mark for 'electrophilic'. However, despite appearances, the reaction is a substitution (of CH_3 for H), not an addition. Candidate B is correct, for 2 marks.

Candidate A

(h)

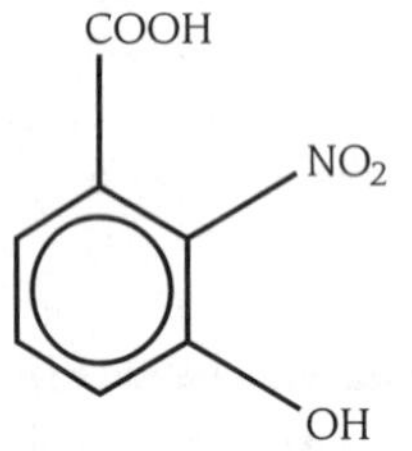

Candidate B

(h)

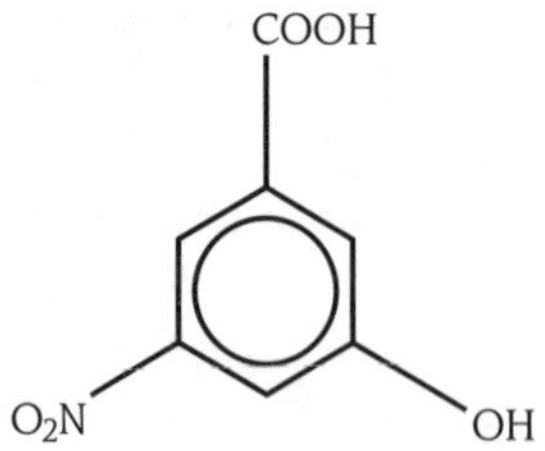

e Both candidates score the mark. Candidate B's answer is a little more likely, as the position next to the –COOH is likely to be slightly blocked by the large group. However, –NO_2 on any spare position satisfies the requirements of the specification.

e **Overall, Candidate A scores 10 marks out of 18. Candidate B scores 16.**

Question 3

Two carbonyl compounds

This question concerns two compounds, A and B, that are isomers of formula C_3H_6O. They are both carbonyl compounds containing a C=O group. Compound A reacts with Benedict's reagent but compound B does not.

(a) Draw the displayed formulae for compounds A and B. Name the compounds and the functional groups they contain. (*Suitably labelled table*) (6 marks)

(b) Give the colour of Benedict's reagent and the result of a positive Benedict's test. (*1 line*). (2 marks)

(c) Using acidified potassium dichromate solution, one of the compounds A or B can be oxidised to a carboxylic acid.
　(i) Name the compound that can be oxidised and give the name and formula of the acid formed. (*1 line*) (2 marks)
　(ii) Describe the colour change that occurs when this reaction takes place. (*1 line*) (1 mark)

(d) Compound B can be made by the oxidation of an alcohol. Give the structural formula of this alcohol and name it. (*space, 1 line*) (2 marks)

(e) Infrared spectroscopy can be used to distinguish between compounds A and B.
　(i) Which part of the molecule gives rise to differences in the infrared spectra of the two compounds? (*1 line*) (1 mark)
　(ii) The horizontal axis of an infrared spectrum is calibrated in wavenumbers, which measure frequency. How is the vertical axis calibrated? (*1 line*) (1 mark)

(f) Compounds A and B both mix readily with water. Suggest a reason for this. (*2 lines*) (1 mark)

(g) The reaction of Brady's reagent with a carbonyl compound can be represented as follows:

$$R-\underset{R}{\overset{O}{\underset{|}{\overset{||}{C}}}} + NH_2-NH-\underset{NO_2}{\overset{NO_2}{\bigcirc}}-NO_2$$

Step 1

$$R-\underset{R}{\overset{OH}{\underset{|}{\overset{|}{C}}}}-NH-NH-\underset{NO_2}{\bigcirc}-NO_2$$

Step 2

$$R-\underset{R}{\overset{}{\underset{|}{C}}}=N-NH-\underset{NO_2}{\bigcirc}-NO_2$$

3

(i) **Describe the type of reaction in step 1 and its mechanism.** (*1 line*) (2 marks)

(ii) **Why is the carbon of the carbonyl group, C=O, attacked in this way?**
 (*2 lines*) (2 marks)

(iii) **Suggest the identity of the other product of step 2.** (*1 line*) (1 mark)

(iv) **Describe the positive result of the test with Brady's reagent.**
 (*1 line*) (1 mark)

Total: 22 marks

■ ■ ■

Candidates' answers to Question 3

Candidate A

(a)

	Compound A	Compound B
	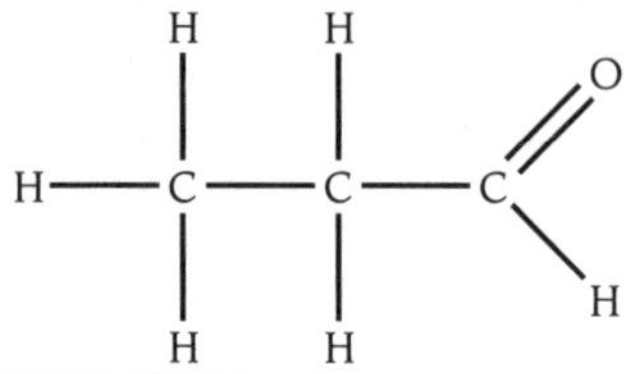	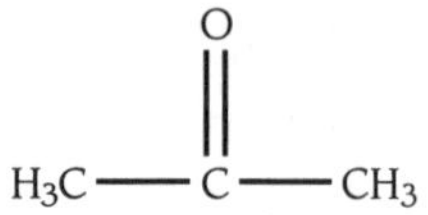
Name of compound	Propan-1-al	Propan-2-one
Functional group	Aldehyde	Ketone

Candidate B

(a)

	Compound A	Compound B
	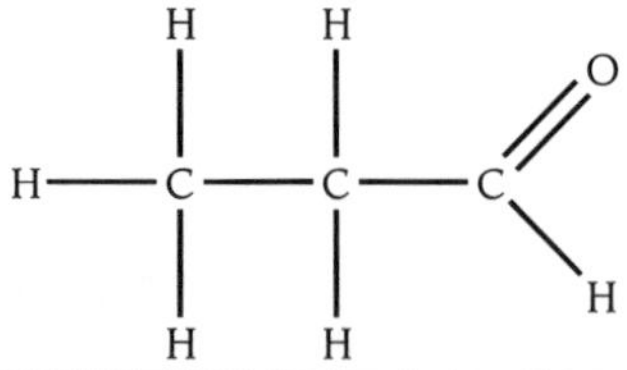	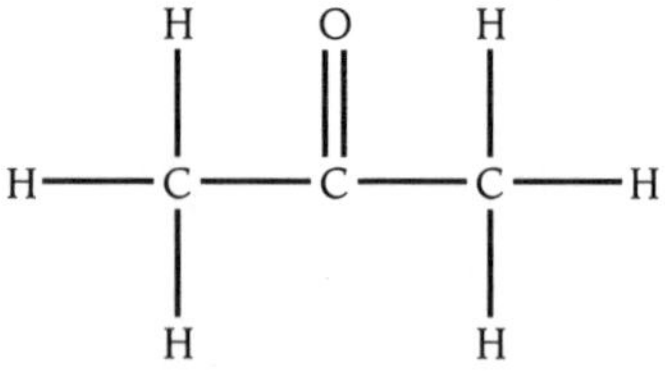
Name of compound	Propanal	Propanone
Functional group	Aldehyde	Ketone

✎ Candidate A has the formulae right but he has not fully displayed the formula of compound B. This must be through carelessness, as he has fully displayed the formula of compound A. He scores 1 out of 2 marks for the formulae. He then loses another mark for putting numbers in the names when they are not needed — the aldehyde group must be on the end of the chain and the ketone group must be in the middle. He does gain 1 mark for the name of compound B by 'transferred error'. The names of the functional groups are correct, so Candidate A scores a total of 4 marks. Candidate B has started well with a full 6 marks.

Candidate A

(b) Benedict's reagent is blue. A red precipitate is produced.

Candidate B

(b) Benedict's reagent is blue. A brown precipitate is produced.

  e Candidate A scores both the marks here. Candidate B is nearly right, but brown is not allowed because it is too similar to the colour with Brady's reagent. She scores 1 mark, for blue. Red-brown is allowable!

Candidate A

(c) (i) Propanal is oxidised to propanoic acid, C_3H_7OOH.

Candidate B

(c) (i) Propanal is oxidised to propanoic acid, C_2H_5COOH.

  e Candidate A identifies the compound correctly. However, there is no mark for this as it is a 50/50 choice! He then names the acid correctly, for 1 mark, but fails to get the formula right. Candidate B gains both marks.

Candidate A

(c) (ii) Yellow to green

Candidate B

(c) (ii) Orange to green

  e Candidate A does not score. Yellow is the colour of potassium *chromate*, not dichromate. Candidate B gives the correct response and gains the mark. Be careful with those colours!

Candidate A

(d) $CH_3CH_2CH_2OH$; propanol

Candidate B

(d) C_3H_7OH; propan-2-ol

  e Candidate A does not score. The formula he has given is the alcohol that is oxidised to propanal (compound A). He then disqualifies himself from any possible 'transferred error' by not putting the number in the name to make it propan-1-ol. Candidate B has the name correct (for 1 mark) but she has not written the formula correctly. Propan-2-ol cannot be represented in this way. C_3H_7OH implies that the $-OH$ group is on the end of the chain. A possible representation is $CH_3CH(OH)CH_3$, or a more displayed formula.

Candidate A

(e) (i) The C–H bond

Candidate B

(e) (i) The carbonyl group

  e Candidate A does not score. The C–H bond *on the carbonyl carbon* of an aldehyde has a different absorption from the other C–H bonds and there is no such bond in ketones. Candidate B just scores, though it would be safer to say 'the C=O bond'. This has a different absorption in aldehydes and ketones.

Candidate A

(e) (ii) It measures absorption.

Candidate B

(e) (ii) Transmission, %

e Candidate A is simply wrong. The axis is calibrated in terms of transmission, so that the 'troughs' indicate absorption. Candidate B scores the mark.

Candidate A

(f) They both form hydrogen bonds with water.

Candidate B

(f) The C=O bond forms hydrogen bonds.

e Candidate A scores the mark even though he has not (as Candidate B has) mentioned the part of the molecule that forms the hydrogen bonds. However, he *has* mentioned the fact that they form these intermolecular forces *with water*, which is necessary to score the mark. Hence, Candidate B does not score. Be sure to give as much detail as possible.

Candidate A

(g) (i) Nucleophilic elimination

Candidate B

(g) (i) Nucleophilic addition

e Candidate B is correct. The elimination follows in step 2. She scores 2 marks and Candidate A scores 1 mark, for nucleophilic.

Candidate A

(g) (ii) C is δ^+ because of the oxygen. The nitrogen is attracted to it.

Candidate B

(g) (ii) The C=O bond is polarised $C^{\delta+}=O^{\delta-}$. The lone pair on the nitrogen is attracted to the δ^+ and forms a covalent bond.

e Candidate A scores the first mark for implying that the C=O bond is polarised, though he does not express this very well. He does not say enough to score the second mark. Candidate B knows the definition of a nucleophile and puts it to good use, to produce an elegant answer to gain the second mark. Therefore, she scores 2 marks.

Candidate A

(g) (iii) H_2O

Candidate B

(g) (iii) Water

e Both candidates score the mark. Step 2 is an elimination reaction and water is lost.

Candidate A

(g) (iv) An orange solid

Candidate B

(g) (iv) An orange-yellow precipitate

e Both candidates score the mark. The precipitate must *not* be described as red (possible confusion with Benedict's again). 'Solid' or 'crystals' would be acceptable instead of 'precipitate'. Once again we see how particular the examiners are about colours. Learn the accepted colours, so that you don't trip up!

e **Overall, Candidate A scores 12 out of 22 marks. Candidate B scores 19.**

Question 4

A blast furnace reaction

The reaction shown below takes place in a blast furnace.

$$C(s) + CO_2(g) \rightleftharpoons 2CO(g) \quad \Delta H^\ominus = +173 \text{ kJ mol}^{-1}$$

(a) (i) Write the expression for the equilibrium constant in terms of partial pressures, K_p. (*space*) (1 mark)

    (ii) What are the units of K_p when pressures are measured in atmospheres? (*1 line*) (1 mark)

(b) Entropy data for the substances in the equation are given below.

Substance	$\Delta S^\ominus$/J mol^{-1} K^{-1}
C(s)	5.7
CO_2(g)	213.6
CO(g)	197.6

    (i) Suggest reasons for the difference between the standard entropies of:
- C(s) and CO_2(g)
- CO_2(g) and CO(g) (*4 lines*) (2 marks)

    (ii) Explain how you could deduce the sign of $\Delta S^\ominus_{system}$ from the nature of the reactants and products in the equation. (*2 lines*) (1 mark)

    (iii) Use the data in the table to calculate a value for $\Delta S^\ominus_{system}$ for the reaction. Include the sign and the units in your answer. (*space*) (2 marks)

(c) (i) Write the expression for $\Delta S^\ominus_{surroundings}$ in terms of $\Delta H^\ominus$ and T and use it to calculate the temperature at which $\Delta S^\ominus_{total}$ is zero. (*space*) (3 marks)

    (ii) What can you say about the value of K_p at this temperature? (*2 lines*) (1 mark)

    (iii) Under what conditions of temperature would the forward reaction in the equation be described as *spontaneous*? (*1 line*) (1 mark)

(d) (i) At a certain temperature, a mixture of 2.0 moles of carbon monoxide and 1.0 mole of carbon dioxide is in equilibrium in contact with solid carbon. The total pressure of the mixture is 1.0 atm. Calculate the value of K_p at this temperature. (*space*) (3 marks)

    (ii) Would the value of K_p increase, decrease or remain the same if the total pressure were raised to 2 atm? Justify your answer. (*3 lines*) (1 mark)

Total: 16 marks

■ ■ ■

Candidates' answers to Question 4

Candidate A

(a) (i) $\dfrac{[CO]^2}{[C][CO_2]}$

Candidate B

(a) (i) $\dfrac{(pCO)^2}{pCO_2}$

e Candidate A does not score the mark. She has made two mistakes. First, square brackets indicate concentrations, which would be correct for K_c but K_p needs partial pressures. Second, neither the concentration nor the partial pressure of a solid varies, so they are not included in either K_c or K_p expressions. Candidate B just scores the mark, though he has not really written the upper term correctly — it should be 'p^2CO'.

Candidate A

(a) (ii) $mol\,dm^{-3}$

Candidate B

(a) (ii) atm

e Candidate A is confused. The logical answer from her expression is 'no units', as there are equal numbers of concentration terms on the top and bottom of the fraction. She does not score the mark. Candidate B is correct, for 1 mark. The units of the top of the fraction are atm^2 and the units of the bottom of the fraction are atm. This cancels to give *atm*.

Candidate A

(b) (i) Solids are more ordered than gases, so carbon has a much lower entropy than CO or CO_2.

Candidate B

(b) (i) There is a more disordered motion in gases than solids, hence the higher entropy of CO_2 compared with C. CO_2 has more atoms and there are more ways of arranging these than the two atoms in CO, so its entropy is higher.

e Candidate A scores 1 mark for a correct statement. However, she does not fully answer the question because she does not compare the entropies of CO and CO_2. Candidate B does this and scores 2 marks.

Candidate A

(b) (ii) More molecules of gas are formed on the right-hand side, so ΔS is positive.

Candidate B

(b) (ii) Solids have lower entropies than gases, so the entropy increases as one molecule of solid turns to a molecule of gas in the reaction.

e Both candidates score the mark. However, Candidate B ought to realise that it is incorrect to refer to a 'molecule' of carbon. He would have been better to scale up his answer and talk about moles, rather than molecules.

Candidate A

(b) (iii) $2 \times 197.6 - 213.6 - 5.7 = +175.9\,J\,mol^{-1}\,K^{-1}$

question 4

Candidate B

(b) (iii) $(2 \times 197.6) - 213.6 - 5.7 = 175.9\,\mathrm{J\,mol^{-1}\,K^{-1}}$

e Candidate A has carried out the calculation correctly and given the correct sign and units. She scores 2 marks. Candidate B has made a careless mistake by leaving out the '+' sign. He gains 1 mark for the correct working, but loses the sign and units mark.

Candidate A

(c) (i) $\Delta S = \dfrac{-\Delta H}{T}$

$$\dfrac{173}{T} = 175.9$$

$$T = \dfrac{173}{175.9} = 0.98°C$$

Candidate B

(c) (i) $\Delta S = \dfrac{-\Delta H}{T}$

$\Delta S_{total} = \Delta S_{system} + \Delta S_{surroundings}$

When $\Delta S_{total} = 0$, $\Delta S_{surroundings} = -\Delta S_{system}$

$$\dfrac{173\,000}{T} = 175.9$$

$$T = 984\,\mathrm{K}$$

e Candidate A has laid her answer out reasonably well. She gives the correct expression for ΔS (which it is important to have learnt!), so she scores the first mark. However, she then makes a very common error by falling into the 'kilojoule trap'. ΔH is measured in $\mathrm{kJ\,mol^{-1}}$ whereas the energy part of the ΔS unit is in joules. Therefore, she loses the second mark. She then forgets that T is measured in K, not °C, so loses the third mark too. Candidate B has the correct answer and scores all 3 marks.

Candidate A
(c) (ii) It would be 1.

Candidate B
(c) (ii) It would be 0.

e Candidate A is correct and scores the mark. There is an equal balance at this temperature. Candidate B probably means the same, but a moment's thought should have convinced him that K_p values can never be zero, since the concentration terms cannot be zero at equilibrium.

Candidate A
(c) (iii) Greater than 1°C

Candidate B

(c) (iii) At temperatures above 984 K

e Both candidates score the mark, though their answers look very different. Candidate A gains her mark by 'transferred error' from (c) (i).

Candidate A

(d) (i) $K_p = 2^2/1 = 4$

Candidate B

(d) (i) partial pressure = mole fraction × total pressure
So, $pCO = 2/3$ atm and $pCO_2 = 1/3$ atm

Thus, $K_p = \dfrac{(2/3)^2}{1/3}$
$= 1.333$ atm

e Candidate A does not realise how numbers of moles are related to partial pressures. She does not score. Candidate B has answered well. However, he has given his answer to too many significant figures. The data are given to only 2 significant figures, so 1.3 is the correct answer. Candidate B scores 2 of the 3 marks available.

Candidate A

(d) (ii) It would stay the same, as K_p is unaffected by pressure.

Candidate B

(d) (ii) There are more molecules of gas on the right-hand side, so an increase in pressure will move the equilibrium position to the left. Therefore, K_p would decrease.

e Candidate B's first sentence is correct, but his second sentence does not follow from it, so he does not score. The equilibrium position moves *because* K_p remains constant. Candidate A is correct and scores the mark. Remember that K_p and K_c do not vary unless the *temperature* is changed.

e **Overall, Candidate A scores 8 out of 16 marks. Candidate B scores 12.**

Question 5

Propanoic acid

(a) Propanoic acid, C_2H_5COOH, is a weak acid.

  (i) Write an equation for the dissociation of propanoic acid in aqueous solution, which shows that the acid is weak. (*space*)   (2 marks)

  (ii) Circle a base in your equation. Justify your choice. (*2 lines*)   (1 mark)

  (iii) Write the expression for the acid dissociation constant, K_a, of propanoic acid. (*space*)   (1 mark)

  (iv) Calculate the pH of $0.10\ mol\ dm^{-3}$ propanoic acid solution. ($K_a = 1.3 \times 10^{-5}\ mol\ dm^{-3}$) (*space*)   (2 marks)

(b) Sodium hydroxide is a strong base. Calculate the pH of $0.05\ mol\ dm^{-3}$ sodium hydroxide solution. The ionisation constant for water, K_w, is $1.00 \times 10^{-14}\ mol^2\ dm^{-6}$. (*space*)   (2 marks)

(c) A student titrates $10.0\ cm^3$ of $0.05\ mol\ dm^{-3}$ propanoic acid with $0.10\ mol\ dm^{-3}$ sodium hydroxide.

  (i) Write an equation for the reaction. (*space*)   (1 mark)

  (ii) Calculate the volume of sodium hydroxide that will react *exactly* with the propanoic acid. (*space*)   (1 mark)

(d) (i) Use your calculations in parts (a), (b) and (c) and your knowledge of titration curves to sketch on graph paper a curve of pH against volume of sodium hydroxide added for the titration in part (c). (*graph paper*)   (3 marks)

  (ii) Name a suitable indicator for this titration and explain why you have chosen it. (*2 lines*)   (2 marks)

(e) Propanoic acid solution and sodium propanoate solution form a buffer solution when they are mixed together. Calculate the pH of a buffer solution made by mixing solutions so that the concentration of propanoic acid is $0.1\ mol\ dm^{-3}$ and sodium propanoate is $0.05\ mol\ dm^{-3}$. You may use the equation:

$$pH = -\log_{10} K_a - \log_{10}([acid]/[base])\quad (space)$$
    (2 marks)

Total: 17 marks

■ ■ ■

Candidates' answers to Question 5

Candidate A

(a) (i) $C_2H_5COOH \rightleftharpoons C_2H_5COO^- + H^+$

Candidate B

(a) (i) $C_2H_5COOH + H_2O \rightleftharpoons C_2H_5COO^- + H_3O^+$

e Both candidates are correct and both score 2 marks. Candidate B has used the fuller form of the equation and Candidate A has used a simplified form. To answer questions like these, you are advised to use the simplified type of equation.

Candidate A

(a) (ii) $C_2H_5COOH \rightleftharpoons (C_2H_5COO^-) + H^+$

$C_2H_5COO^-$ accepts a proton to become CH_3COOH.

Candidate B

(a) (ii) $C_2H_5COOH + (H_2O) \rightleftharpoons C_2H_5COO^- + H_3O^+$

H_2O accepts a proton from C_2H_5COOH.

e These are both correct answers, so both candidates score the mark.

Candidate A

(a) (iii) $K_a = \dfrac{[C_2H_5COO^-][H^+]}{[C_2H_5COOH]}$

Candidate B

(a) (iii) $K_a = \dfrac{[C_2H_5COO^-][H_3O^+]}{[C_2H_5COOH][H_2O]}$

e Candidate A is correct and scores the mark. Candidate B's answer looks correct in terms of a K_c. However, since water is the solvent, $[H_2O]$ is large and constant, so it is omitted from the expression. K_a is defined as in Candidate A's answer. This is why, in such questions, you are advised to use the type of equation given in Candidate A's answer to (a) (i). Candidate B does not score.

Candidate A

(a) (iv) $pH = -\log_{10}[H^+]$

Here $pH = -\log_{10}(1 \times 10^{-1}) = 1.0$

Candidate B

(a) (iv) For a weak acid, $[H^+] = \sqrt{(K_a \times [HA])} = \sqrt{(1.3 \times 10^{-5} \times 1 \times 10^{-1})}$

$= \sqrt{(1.3 \times 10^{-6})} = 1.14 \times 10^{-3}$

$pH = -\log_{10}(1.14 \times 10^{-3}) = 2.9$

e Candidate A has defined pH correctly. However, he has forgotten that the acid is not fully dissociated in solution, so his value for $[H^+]$ is wrong and he does not score. Candidate B has rearranged the equation for K_a (or learnt the expression!) and used it correctly to calculate the correct value. She scores 2 marks.

Candidate A

(b) $[OH^-] = 0.05$

Thus $[H^+] = \dfrac{1 \times 10^{-14}}{0.05} = 2 \times 10^{-13}\,mol\,dm^{-3}$

Candidate B

(b) $pH = -\log_{10}(K_w/[OH^-]) = 12.7$

e Candidate A starts well and then stops! He forgot that he had to calculate pH, not $[H^+]$. He scores 1 mark. Candidate B is correct, for 2 marks.

5

question

Candidate A

(c) (i) $C_2H_5COOH + NaOH \longrightarrow C_2H_5COONa + H_2O$

Candidate B

(c) (i) $C_2H_5COOH + OH^- \longrightarrow C_2H_5COO^- + H_2O$

e These are correct alternative answers. Both candidates gain the mark.

Candidate A

(c) (ii) moles NaOH = $10 \times 0.05/1000 = 5 \times 10^{-4}$ = moles propanoic acid
volume of sodium hydroxide = $5 \times 10^{-4} \times 1000/0.1 = 5\,cm^3$

Candidate B

(c) (ii) Since they react 1 mole:1 mole, half as much sodium hydroxide will be required,
i.e. $5\,cm^3$

e Both are correct and score the mark. If you find these calculations quite hard, follow
Candidate A's method, slowly and carefully. If you find such things easier, use intuitive
reasoning like Candidate B.

Candidate A

(d) (i)

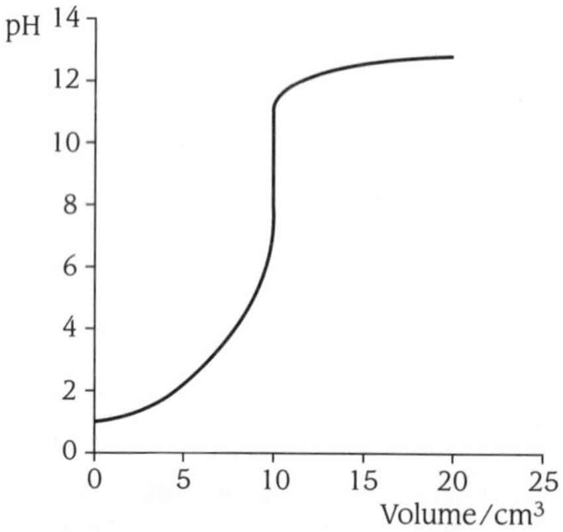

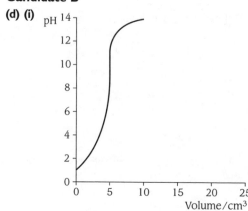

Candidate B

(d) (i)

e The three marks here are for:
- the start and finish at the calculated pH values
- end point at the correct value
- correct shape

Candidate A starts at *his* calculated pH for the acid and ends at a reasonable value for the NaOH, so he scores the first mark. However, he has not taken note of his calculation of the end point, so he misses the second mark. The shape is acceptable (more of a gradual rise at first where the weak acid is in excess, than after the end point when the strong base is in excess), so he scores the third mark.

Candidate B scores the second and third marks but fails to gain the first, since she has not been careful enough about where the pH starts and finishes and has not used her calculated values.

Candidate A
(d) (ii) Universal indicator since the pH is not exactly 7.

Candidate B
(d) (ii) Phenolphthalein, since it changes colour over the range pH 8–10.

e Candidate A is wrong and does not score. Universal indicator is a mixture of indicators and is only used to give an approximate value for the pH of a solution. For a titration, a *single* indicator is always used. Phenolphthalein is used here for the reason given by Candidate B, who scores 2 marks.

Candidate A
(e) $pH = 4.89 - \log_{10}(0.5) = 4.89 + 0.30 = 5.19$

Candidate B
(e) $pH = 4.89 - 0.30 = 4.59$

e Candidate A starts well and makes it clear what he is doing. However, he gets the ratio of [acid]/[base] the wrong way up — it should be 2.0, not 0.5. This is clear from his working, so he scores 1 out of the 2 marks available. Candidate B gives less indication of method but scores 2 marks because the answer is correct.

e **Overall, Candidate A scores 10 marks out of 17. Candidate B scores 15.**